Student Solutions Manual

for use with

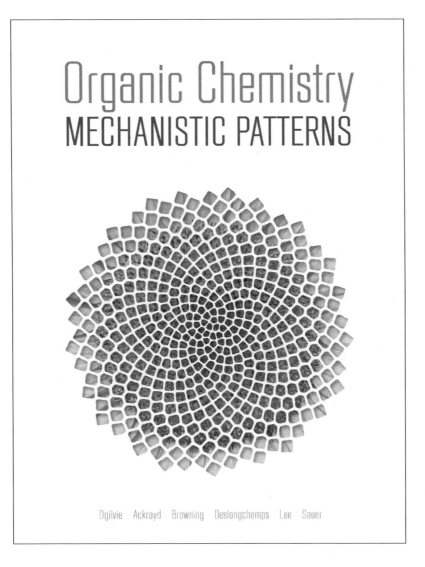

Organic Chemistry
MECHANISTIC PATTERNS

Ogilvie   Ackroyd   Browning   Deslongchamps   Lee   Sauer

Prepared by **Neil Dryden**
University of New Brunswick

and **Nathan Ackroyd**
Mount Royal University

NELSON

NELSON

**Student Solutions Manual
for use with Organic Chemistry**

prepared by Neil Dryden and
Nathan Ackroyd

**VP, Product and Partnership
Solutions:**
Anne Williams

**Senior Publisher, Digital and Print
Content:**
Paul Fam

Marketing Manager:
Terry Fedorkiw

Technical Reviewer:
Philip Dutton

Content Manager:
Katherine Goodes

Senior Production Project Manager:
Imoinda Romain

ISBN-13: 978-0-17-670274-8
ISBN-10: 0-17-670274-1

Table of Contents

Chapter 1
Carbon and Its Compounds

PROBLEMS

1.13

a) Hydrogen has one electron. In the ground state, it is contained in the 1s orbital. An electron in the 2s orbital would have to be an excited state of the hydrogen atom.

b) Carbon has six electrons. Its electron configuration is $1s^2 2s^2 2p^2$. Therefore, the valence electrons are in 2s and 2p orbitals. The 1s orbital is a core orbital.

1.15

a)
```
      H  H
      |  |
   H–C–N–H
      |  ··
      H
```

b)
```
   H  H  H  H  H
   |  |  |  |  |
   H–C–C=C–C–C–H
      |     |  |
      H     H  H
```

c)   H−C≡C−H

d)
```
   H  H  H
   |  |  |
   H–C–C–C=O:
      |  |    ··
      H  H
```

e)
```
   H  H  H
   |  |  | ⊕
   H–C–C–O–H
      |  |  ··
      H  H
```

f)
```
   H  H  ··  H  H
   |  |      |  |
   H–C–C–N–C–C–H
   |  |  |  |  |
   H  H  |  H  H
         H–C–H
            |
         H–C–H
            |
            H
```

g)
```
      H
      |
   H–C–C≡N:
      |
      H
```

h)
```
          H
          |
      H:O:H
      |  |  |
   H–C–C–C–H
      |  |  |
      H  H  H
```

i)   An intermediate structure is useful in determining the final structure.

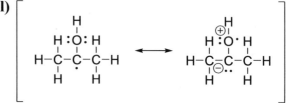

$3(3H) + 8(2C) + 5(N) + 6(O) = 22\ e^-$
$22\ e^- - 12\ bonding\ e^- = 10\ LP\ e^-$

j)

$$\begin{array}{c}
\text{H} \\
| \\
\text{H--C--H} \\
\\
\text{H} \quad | \quad \text{H} \\
| \quad\quad | \\
\text{H--C--C--C--H} \\
| \quad \oplus \quad | \\
\text{H} \quad\quad \text{H}
\end{array}$$

l)

$$\left[\ \begin{array}{ccc}
\text{H} & & \text{H} \\
| & & \oplus| \\
\text{H:O:H} & \longleftrightarrow & \text{H:O·H} \\
| & & | \\
\text{H--C--C--C--H} & & \text{H--C--C--C--H} \\
| \quad\; \bullet \quad\; | & & |\;\;\ominus\;\; | \\
\text{H} \quad\quad \text{H} & & \text{H} \quad\quad \text{H}
\end{array}\ \right]$$

k)

$$\begin{array}{c}
\text{H} \;\; \text{H} \\
| \quad\; | \\
\text{H--C--C--O:}^{\ominus} \\
| \quad\; | \\
\text{H} \;\; \text{H}
\end{array}$$

1.17

a)   A molecule of formula C_2H_5N having no formal charge on any atom:

$$\begin{array}{c}
\text{H} \\
| \\
\text{H--C--N--H} \\
| \quad\; | \\
\text{H} \;\; \text{H}
\end{array}$$

b)   A cation of formula $C_2H_8N^+$:

$$\begin{array}{c}
\text{H} \;\; \text{H} \;\; \text{H} \\
| \quad\; \oplus| \quad\; | \\
\text{H--C--N--C--H} \\
| \quad\; | \quad\; | \\
\text{H} \;\; \text{H} \;\; \text{H}
\end{array}$$

c)   An anion of formula $C_2F_3O^-$ having a C=O bond:

$$\begin{array}{c}
:\text{F}: \text{O}: \\
| \quad\; || \\
:\text{F--C--C}: \\
| \\
:\text{F}:^{\ominus}
\end{array}$$

d)   Two neutral molecules of formula C_2H_3N, both having a C–N triple bond:

$$\begin{array}{c}
\text{H} \\
| \\
\text{H--C--C}\equiv\text{N}: \\
| \\
\text{H}
\end{array}
\qquad
\begin{array}{c}
\text{H} \quad \oplus \;\; \ominus \\
| \\
\text{H--C--N}\equiv\text{C}: \\
| \\
\text{H}
\end{array}$$

1.19

a)

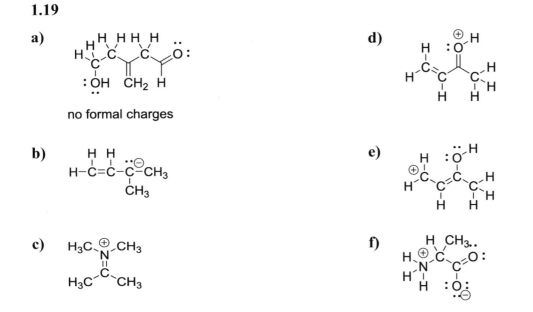

no formal charges

b)

H H   ..
H–C=C–C⊖–CH₃
        |
        CH₃

c)

H₃C ⊕ CH₃
    N
    ‖
    C
H₃C   CH₃

d)

         ⊕
         :O–H
H |
 C   C–H
H   C   H
    |
    H   H

e)

         ..
         :O–H
 ⊕ H |
  C   C–H
H   C   H
    |
    H   H

f)

     H CH₃ ..
H ⊕ C   O:
 N   ‖
H | C
  H   :O:
      ..⊖

1.21

Electronegativities are provided in Figure 1.6.

a) The N–H bond would be more polar due to the larger electronegativity difference between N(3.0) and H(2.2) than between B(2.0) and H(2.2). The distinction between them is that the N–H bond is polarized toward the nitrogen, while the B–H bond is polarized toward the hydrogen.

b) i)   ii)   iii)   iv)

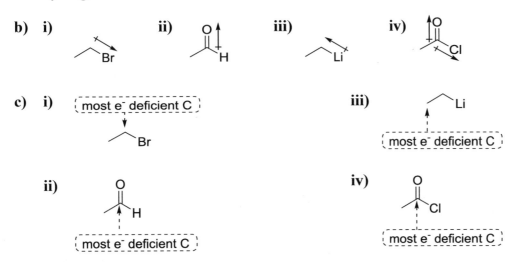

c) i)   ┌ ─ ─ ─ ─ ─ ─ ─ ─ ─ ─ ─ ┐
         ┊ most e⁻ deficient C ┊
         └ ─ ─ ─ ─ ─ ─ ─ ─ ─ ─ ─ ┘
                  ↓
               Br

    iii)   Li
         ┌ ─ ─ ─ ─ ─ ─ ─ ─ ─ ─ ─ ┐
         ┊ most e⁻ deficient C ┊
         └ ─ ─ ─ ─ ─ ─ ─ ─ ─ ─ ─ ┘

    ii)   O
              ‖
              C
                 H
         ┌ ─ ─ ─ ─ ─ ─ ─ ─ ─ ─ ─ ┐
         ┊ most e⁻ deficient C ┊
         └ ─ ─ ─ ─ ─ ─ ─ ─ ─ ─ ─ ┘

    iv)   O
              ‖
              C
                 Cl
         ┌ ─ ─ ─ ─ ─ ─ ─ ─ ─ ─ ─ ┐
         ┊ most e⁻ deficient C ┊
         └ ─ ─ ─ ─ ─ ─ ─ ─ ─ ─ ─ ┘

1.23

a)

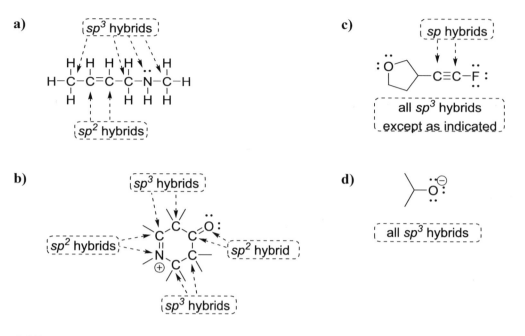

b)

c)

d)

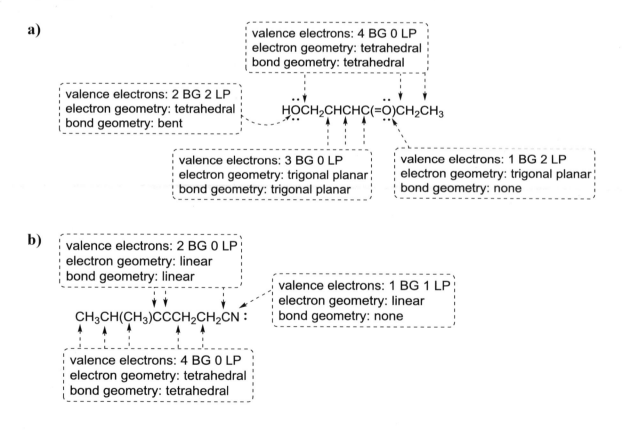

1.25

In each diagram, the hybridization, electron pair geometry, and bond geometry for the non-hydrogen atoms are indicated.

a)

valence electrons: 4 BG 0 LP
electron geometry: tetrahedral
bond geometry: tetrahedral

valence electrons: 2 BG 2 LP
electron geometry: tetrahedral
bond geometry: bent

HOCH₂CHCHC(=O)CH₂CH₃

valence electrons: 3 BG 0 LP
electron geometry: trigonal planar
bond geometry: trigonal planar

valence electrons: 1 BG 2 LP
electron geometry: trigonal planar
bond geometry: none

b)

valence electrons: 2 BG 0 LP
electron geometry: linear
bond geometry: linear

valence electrons: 1 BG 1 LP
electron geometry: linear
bond geometry: none

CH₃CH(CH₃)CCCH₂CH₂CN :

valence electrons: 4 BG 0 LP
electron geometry: tetrahedral
bond geometry: tetrahedral

c)

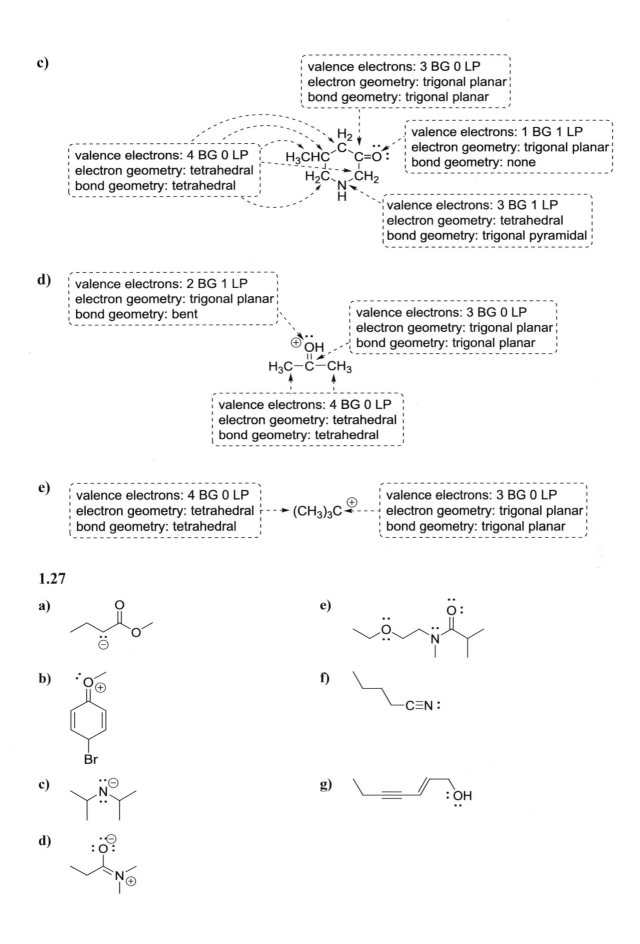

valence electrons: 3 BG 0 LP
electron geometry: trigonal planar
bond geometry: trigonal planar

valence electrons: 1 BG 1 LP
electron geometry: trigonal planar
bond geometry: none

valence electrons: 4 BG 0 LP
electron geometry: tetrahedral
bond geometry: tetrahedral

valence electrons: 3 BG 1 LP
electron geometry: tetrahedral
bond geometry: trigonal pyramidal

d)

valence electrons: 2 BG 1 LP
electron geometry: trigonal planar
bond geometry: bent

valence electrons: 3 BG 0 LP
electron geometry: trigonal planar
bond geometry: trigonal planar

valence electrons: 4 BG 0 LP
electron geometry: tetrahedral
bond geometry: tetrahedral

e)

valence electrons: 4 BG 0 LP
electron geometry: tetrahedral
bond geometry: tetrahedral

valence electrons: 3 BG 0 LP
electron geometry: trigonal planar
bond geometry: trigonal planar

1.27

a)

e)

b)

f)

c)

g)

d)

1.29

a)
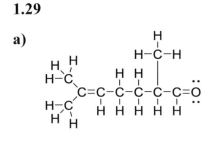

b)
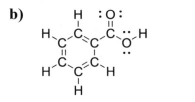

c)
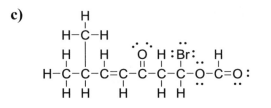

1.31

a)
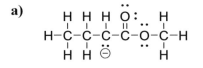

b)
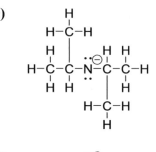

1.33

a)
 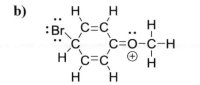

b)
 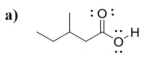

d)
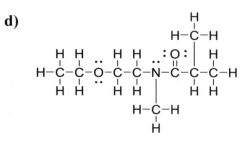

e)
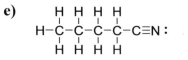

f)
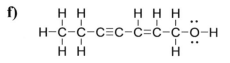

c)
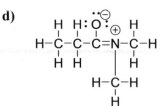

d)
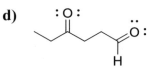

c)
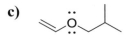

d)
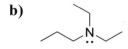

1.35

a) The geometry at each non-H atom in the above molecule appears below. Carbons are numbered in the diagram for clarity.

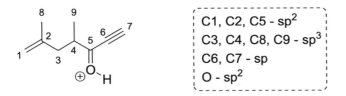

C1, C2, C5 - trigonal planar
C3, C4, C8, C9 - tetrahedral
C6, C7 - linear
O - bent (120°)

b) Hybridizations for each non-H atom:

C1, C2, C5 - sp^2
C3, C4, C8, C9 - sp^3
C6, C7 - sp
O - sp^2

Bond descriptions:

Bond 1 – C sp^3- C sp^2 σ-bond

Bond 2 – C sp^2- C sp^2 σ-bond
+ C p- C p π-bond

Bond 3 – C sp^3- C sp^3 σ-bond

Bond 4 – C sp^3- C sp^2 σ-bond

Bond 5 – C sp^2- C sp σ-bond

Bond 6 – O sp^2- H s σ-bond

1.37

a) Boron has three valence electrons.

b) Lewis structure and geometry of BH_3:

H
|
H-B-H   trigonal planar

c) Hybridization of a boron atom:

H
|
H-B-H ←----- sp^2 hybridization

Boron has an incomplete octet, since there are only three shared bond pairs with hydrogen atoms.

MCAT Style Problems

1.39

Answer: (a). There is an undrawn H atom implied on the carbon atom in this representation.

Challenge Problem

1.41

Assigning the valence electrons as single bonds and lone pairs would lead to the following intermediate Lewis structure:

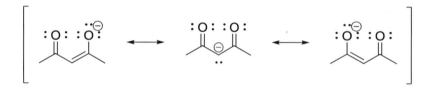

Forming bonds with the lone pairs to reduce the formal charges would lead to the resonance forms for the molecule, as shown below.

This shows that the two oxygen atoms and the central carbon atom have negative charges in one of the resonance forms. They will be the most likely sites to act as electron donors in reactions.

Chapter 2
Anatomy of an Organic Molecule

PROBLEMS

2.15 For unsaturated molecules, the site of unsaturation is indicated in the structures shown.

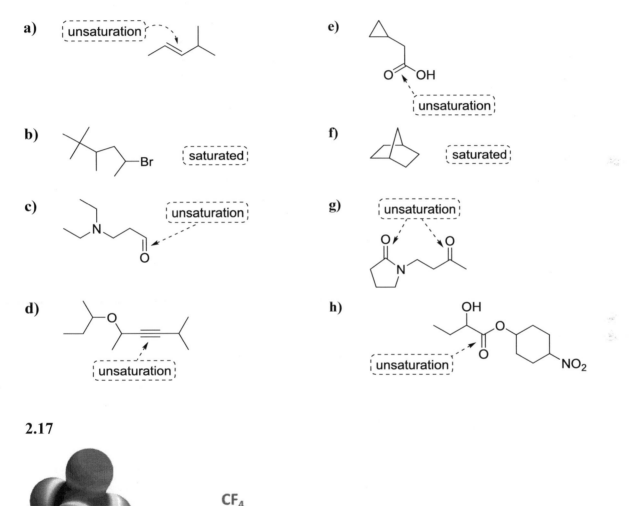

2.17

CF$_4$

The electron density is concentrated on the fluorine atoms (outer regions; red in the textbook) since fluorine is highly electronegative and attracts electron density away from the carbon atom (central region; blue in the textbook). In methane, the charge density is evenly distributed, since carbon and hydrogen have similar electronegativities.

2.19

The intermolecular forces would involve hydrogen bonding from the carboxylic acid groups. This would be similar for both molecules. The only difference would be in the dispersion forces between the hydrocarbon chains. Line drawings of both would look like:

The alkane region in 2-ethylhexanoic acid is seven carbons long, while it is only five in hexanoic acid. This would result in more attractions in 2-ethylhexanoic acid and, therefore, 2-ethylhexanoic acid should have a higher boiling point.

2.21

Molecules ranked in the expected order of increasing solubility in water:

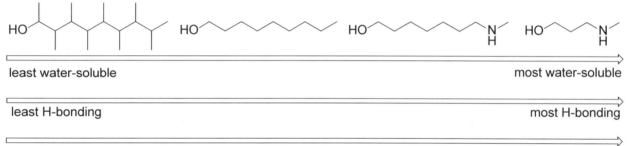

The two most soluble molecules have two hydrogen bonding groups on them. The smaller of the two will be most soluble, since it has a smaller hydrophobic region. The two least-soluble molecules have one hydrogen bonding group, but the least-soluble one has a much larger hydrophobic region due to the extra methyl substituents.

2.23

Carbons in the main chain are numbered in some diagrams to assist in naming.

a)

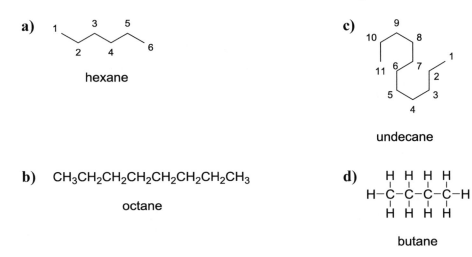

hexane

c)

undecane

b) CH₃CH₂CH₂CH₂CH₂CH₂CH₂CH₃

octane

d)

butane

2.25

Carbons in the main chain are numbered in some diagrams to assist in naming.

a) This might also be referred to as "4-(*n*-butyl)-3-methyldecane."

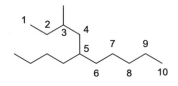

4-(1-butyl)-3-methyldecane

b) Converting condensed structure to a line structure makes naming easier.

CH₃CH₂CCH₃CH₂CH₂CH(CH(CH₃)₂)CH₂CH₂CH₃

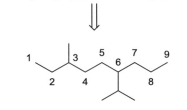

3-methyl-6-(2-propyl)nonane

c)

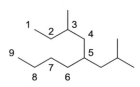

3-methyl-5-(2-methylpropyl)nonane
or
3-methyl-5-isobutylnonane

d)

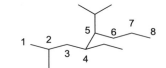

4-ethyl-2-methyl-5-(2-propyl)octane

2.27

Parts (a) through (h) refer to this molecule.

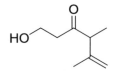

Answers to (a), (b), (c), and (e) appear in the diagram below.

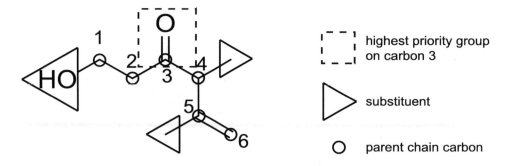

	highest priority group on carbon 3
	substituent
	parent chain carbon

d)   Root name: hex-5-en-3-one

f)   Substituents: C1 hydroxy, C4 methyl, C5 methyl

g)   1-hydroxy-4,5-dimethyl

h)   1-hydroxy-4,5-dimethylhex-5-en-3-one

2.29

Carbons in the main chain are numbered in some diagrams to assist in naming.

a)

3-fluoro-2,4-dimethylheptane

d)

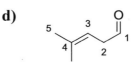

4-methylpent-3-enal

b)

OH
1   5
3
2   4

3-pentanol

e)

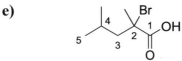

2-bromo-2,4-dimethylpentanoic acid

c)

OH
1
2   4
3

2-ethyl-1-butanol

2.31

In order for a substituent to not be a functional group, it would have to be an alkyl group. An ethyl group would be an example of this. A functional group is not a substituent if it is the highest priority group in the molecule and, therefore, the basis for the name of the molecule. The carboxylic acid group in 3-chlorobutanoic acid would be an example of this.

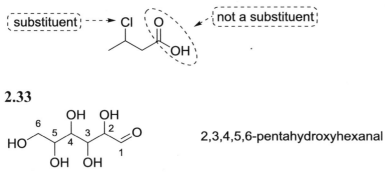

2.33

OH   OH
6
5   3   2   O
HO   4
1
OH   OH

2,3,4,5,6-pentahydroxyhexanal

2.35

a) **i)** 2-methylpropan-1-al prefix: 2-methyl root: propan suffix: 1-al
    ii) 2,3-dichlorocyclopent-1-ene prefix: 2,3-dichloro
root: cyclopent
suffix: 1-ene

    iii) heptan-3-ol prefix: none root: heptan suffix: 3-ol
    iv) 5,6-diethyl-7-hydroxyoct-1-yn-3-one prefix: 5,6-diethyl-7-hydroxy
root: oct-1-yn
suffix: 3-one

b) **i)** aldehyde (-al)　　　　　　**iii)** alcohol (-ol)
　　　ii) alkene (-ene)　　　　　　**iv)** ketone (-one)

c) **i)** prop = 3 carbon chain　　　**iii)** hept = 7 carbon chain
　　　　　C=O double bond at C1　　　　　　no multiple bonds
　　　ii) pent = 5 carbon chain　　　**iv)** oct = 8 carbon chain C≡C triple bond
　　　　　C=C double bond at C1　　　　　　at C1 C=O double bond at C3

d) **i)** methyl group at C2　　　　　**iii)** no substituents
　　　ii) chloro group at C2 chloro group at C3　　**iv)** ethyl group at C5 ethyl group at C6
　　　　　　　　　　　　　　　　　　　　　　hydroxyl group at C7

e) **i)**

2-methylpropan-1-al

ii)

2,3-dichlorocyclopent-1-ene

iii)

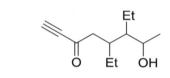

heptan-3-ol

iv)

5,6-diethyl-7-hydroxyoct-1-yn-3-one

2.37

a)

butanoic acid

b)

4-propoxybutanoic acid

c)

3-methylbut-2-enoic acid

d)

2-ethylpent-3-ynoic acid

MCAT Style Problems

2.39

Answer: (b).

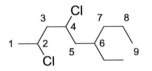

1-cyclohexylpropan-2-one

For (a), 2-oxo-propylbenzene, there is no aromatic ring. Answer (c), 1-cyclohexylacetaldehyde, is a ketone, not an aldehyde. For (d), 2-oxo-propylcyclohexane, the highest-priority group is the ketone, so the suffix should be *-one*.

2.41

Answer: (d).

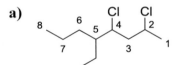

2,4-dichloro-5-ethylnonane

a)

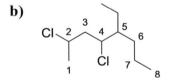

2,4-dichloro-5-ethyloctane

c)

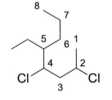

2,4-dichloro-5-ethyloctane

b)

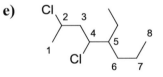

2,4-dichloro-5-ethyloctane

e)

2,4-dichloro-5-ethyloctane

Challenge Problems

2.43

a)

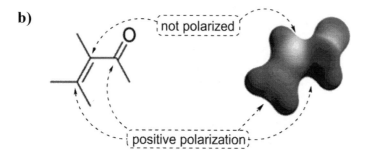

3,4-dimethylpent-3-en-2-one

b)

The electrostatic map shows that the carbon nearest the oxygen and the one on the double bond furthest from the oxygen are positively polarized, while the middle one is more neutral. The one closest to the oxygen is electron deficient, due to the electronegative oxygen drawing electron density away from it. The second resonance form (shown below) shows a formal charge on the other electron deficient carbon, explaining its lack of electron density.

2.44

a)

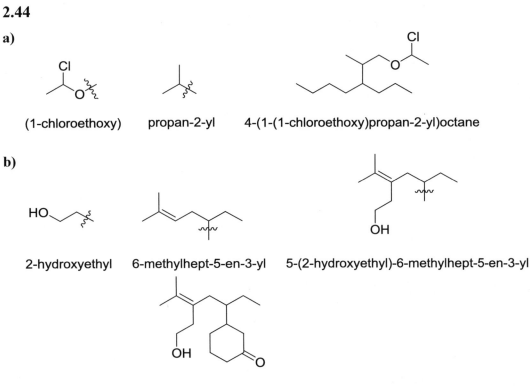

(1-chloroethoxy) propan-2-yl 4-(1-(1-chloroethoxy)propan-2-yl)octane

b)

2-hydroxyethyl 6-methylhept-5-en-3-yl 5-(2-hydroxyethyl)-6-methylhept-5-en-3-yl

3-(5-(2-hydroxyethyl)-6-methylhept-5-en-3-yl)cyclohexan-1-one

2.45

The main chain is numbered and the various substituents are identified in the figure below. The isopropyl groups need to be expanded into line-drawing form to correctly name the molecule.

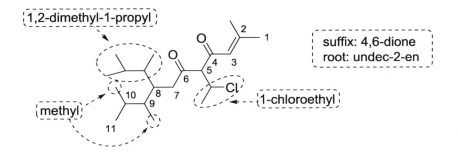

The systematic name would then be: 5-(1-chloroethyl)-9,10-dimethyl-8-(1,2-dimethyl-1-propyl)undec-2-en-4,6-dione.

Chapter 3
Molecules in Motion:
Conformations by Rotations

PROBLEMS

3.13

a) The conformations of a molecule are different forms produced by rotations around single bonds.

b) A conformer of a molecule is generated by single bond rotations. An isomer of a molecule requires breaking bonds to produce it.

3.15

Lewis structures by definition do not depict geometry, just connectivity. So, there would be no way to show different conformations.

3.17

a)

b)

c)

d)

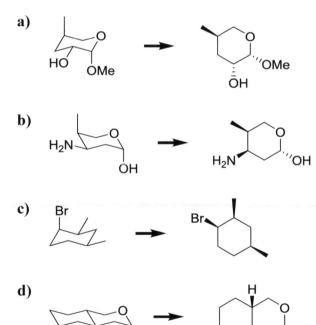

3.19

a)

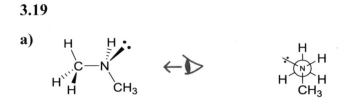

b) The graph would resemble that of ethane. All eclipsed conformations have the same interactions and would have the same strain energy.

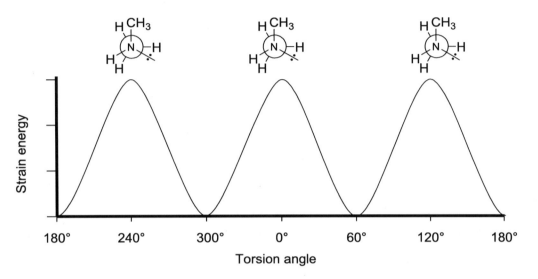

c) All eclipsed conformers have the same energy. All staggered conformers have the same energy.

d) All barriers are the same height.

e) The barriers would be lower for CH_3NH_2, since the bulkier methyl group has been replaced with a smaller hydrogen atom.

3.21

a) The staggered conformations at 60° and 300° have equivalent interactions and are lower in energy than the 180° conformation. The 0° conformation is the lowest energy eclipsed conformation (methyl-hydrogen interaction), while the 120° and 240° conformers are equivalent and higher in energy (methyl–methyl interaction).

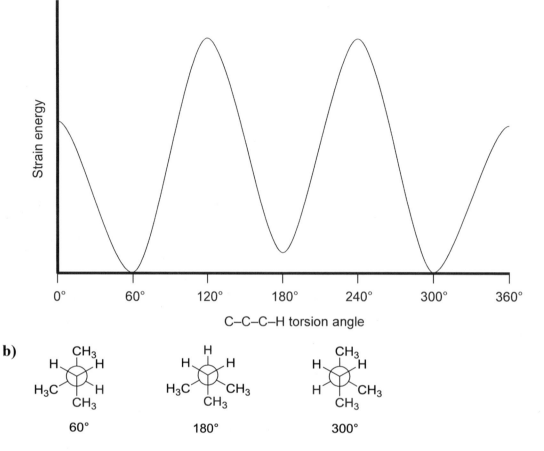

C–C–C–H torsion angle

b)

60°   180°   300°

c) The staggered conformations at 60° and 300° have equivalent interactions and are lower in energy than the 180° conformation. The main difference is that the front methyl has staggered interactions, with an H and a CH_3 at 60° and 300°, while at 180° the front methyl has interactions with two CH_3 groups.

d) The 0° conformation is the only eclipsed conformation with the lowest energy. The other two eclipsed conformations have methyl–methyl interactions.

3.23

a) The equatorial form of *cis*-1,3-dimethylcyclobutane would be more stable, since it maximizes the distance of the larger methyl groups from other groups in the molecule. As well, in the axial form, the two methyl groups exhibit both torsional and steric strain.

equatorial   axial

b) Both conformers of *trans*-1,3-dimethylcyclobutane would have equivalent interactions. They are exactly the same in different orientations.

3.25

a) The steric interactions are between a hydrogen and a methyl group in the same geometry in both cases. Therefore, the strain should be the same: ~0.9 kcal/mol. Hydrogen atoms are too small to create any significant steric strain through H–H interactions, so the total steric strain should be ~0.9 kcal/mol for the gauche conformation of butane.

b) There are two hydrogen atoms in an axial geometry that would interact with the axial methyl group in the conformer of methylcyclohexane drawn. So, this conformer would have 2 × 0.9, or 1.8 kcal/mol, of steric strain from H–methyl interactions.

3.27

a)

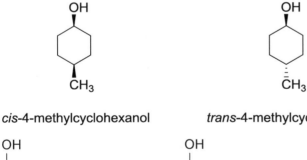

cis-4-methylcyclohexanol   *trans*-4-methylcyclohexanol

b)

cis
axial OH

trans
axial OH

c)

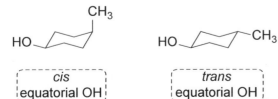

cis
equatorial OH

trans
equatorial OH

d) In part (b), the difference in the axial OH conformers would be *trans*, having 1.8 kcal/mol more strain arising from the CH$_3$ group being axial.

In part (c), the difference in the equatorial OH conformers would be *cis*, having 1.8 kcal/mol more strain arising from the CH$_3$ group being axial.

The *cis* form would be most stable, having an axial OH and equatorial CH$_3$.

The *trans* form would be most stable, having equatorial OH and CH$_3$.

3.29

3.31

The gauche conformers have the two large chlorine atoms close to each other. By increasing the distance between them (60° → 67°, 300° → 293°), the Cl–Cl repulsions can be reduced. The H–H interactions should not increase significantly due to the small size of the hydrogen.

3.33

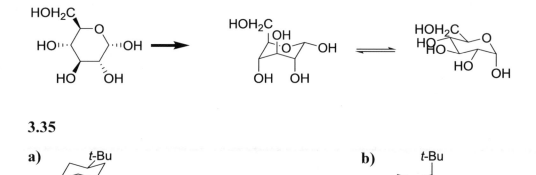

3.35

a)

b)

c) The conformer in (a) would be lower energy. The very large tertiary butyl group creates the most steric strain and would be most stable in an equatorial position to reduce the strain.

d)

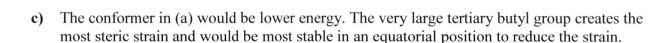

3.37

Taking the number 1 carbon as reference, the five isomers can be described by the relative orientation of the 2,4,5 methyl groups (*cis* or *trans*). The five unique isomers are shown below.

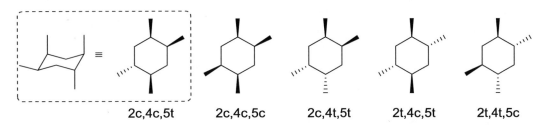

| 2c,4c,5t | 2c,4c,5c | 2c,4t,5t | 2t,4c,5t | 2t,4t,5c |

3.39

a)

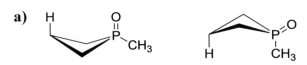

b) Since there are different 1,3 diaxial interactions (=O,H or CH_3,H), the strain is most likely different in each conformer.

3.41

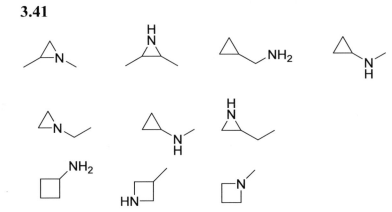

3.43

There are no chair or half-chair conformations in the inversion process.

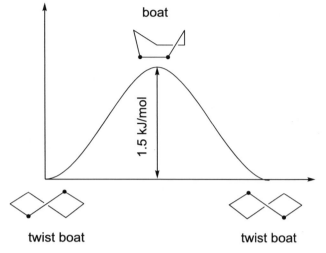

3.45

Cyclopropene would have more strain. The hybrid orbitals forming the σ-bonds (60° bond angles) are sp² and 120° apart on the alkene carbons. This would lead to poorer overlap than in cyclopropane where all of the σ-bond formation is with sp³ orbitals with 109° angles.

3.47

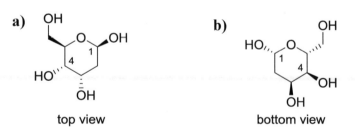

3.49

a)   In cyclopropane, two of the bonds on each carbon are strained. In tetrahedrane, three of them are strained. So, the total strain energy would be expected to be 4 × cyclopropane + strain from third bond + loss of stability from one unstrained C–H bond.

b)   Although the total strain in cubane is more, each carbon atom would undergo less strain than in tetrahedrane. The bond angles are 90°, which is closer to the preferred 109° for sp³ hybridization. So, the C–C bonds should be stronger and the molecule more stable as a result.

MCAT Style Problems

3.51

Answer: (d). Only statement (iii) is true.

i) False. This is steric strain.

ii) False. Torsional strain exists due to eclipsed C–H bonds.

3.53

Answer: (d). None of the statements is true.

i) False. The half-chair conformation is the highest energy.

ii) False. Conformers are configurations of the same isomer.

iii) False. Conformational changes cannot change molecules into different isomers.

Challenge Problems

3.55

a)

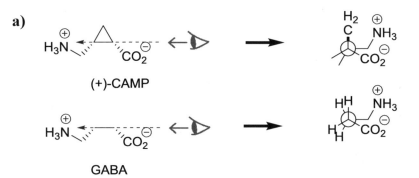

Allowing the oppositely charged functional groups to get as close as possible would be a strong stabilizing influence. It is likely that GABA, which has no restricted rotation, would adopt a conformation that maximizes this interaction.

b) This is a different conformation. The ring prevents the charged functional groups from forming the conformation where they are eclipsed.

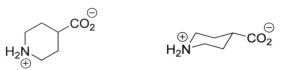

c) The two functional groups are *trans*. This is a similar conformation to (b).

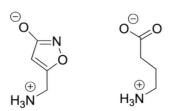

3.56

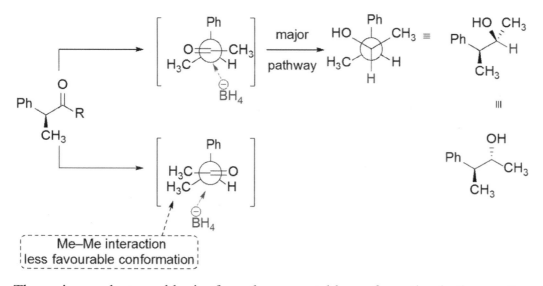

The major product would arise from the more stable conformation in the reactive step.

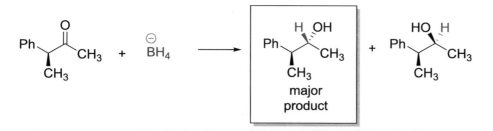

Chapter 4
Stereochemistry:
Three-Dimensional Structure in Molecules

PROBLEMS

4.29

Chirality centres are indicated by an asterisk (*).

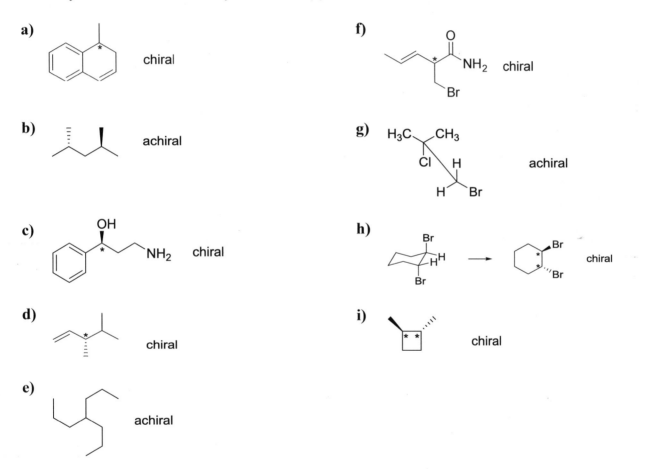

a)
  chiral

b)
  achiral

c)
  chiral

d)
  chiral

e)
  achiral

f)
  chiral

g)
  achiral

h)
  chiral

i)
  chiral

4.31

Chirality centres are marked with an asterisk (*).

a)

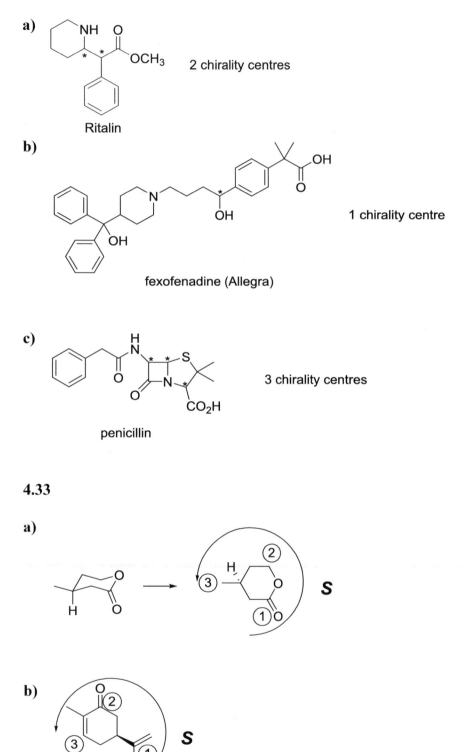

2 chirality centres

Ritalin

b)

1 chirality centre

fexofenadine (Allegra)

c)

3 chirality centres

penicillin

4.33

a)

S

b)

S

c)

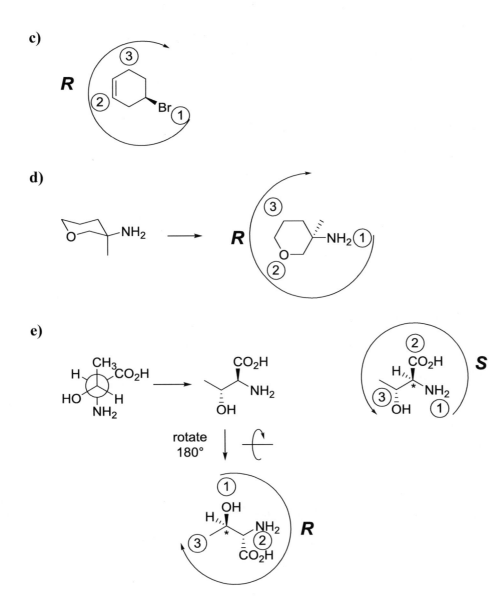

d)

e)

f)

g)

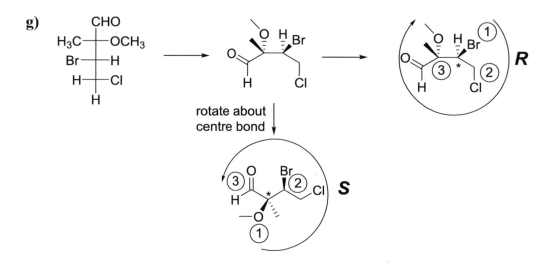

rotate about
centre bond

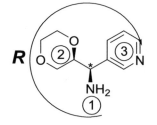

h)

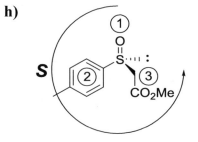

i)

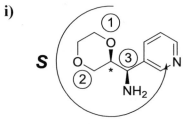

j)

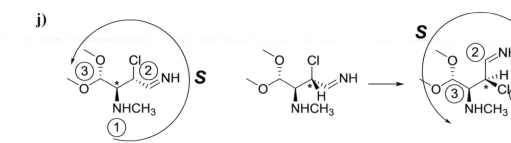

4.35

Concentration in g/100 mL:

$$c = \frac{2.6\ \text{g}}{10.0\ \text{mL}} = 0.26\ \frac{\text{g}}{\text{mL}} = 26.0\ \frac{\text{g}}{100\ \text{mL}}$$

Pathlength in dm:

$$l = 1.0\ \text{cm} \times \frac{1\ \text{dm}}{10\ \text{cm}} = 0.10\ \text{dm}$$

Specific rotation:

$$[\alpha]_D = \frac{100 \cdot \alpha}{c \cdot l} = \frac{100 \times +1.73°}{26.0\ \frac{g}{100\ mL} \times 0.10\ dm} = +66.5$$

So, the specific rotation would be reported as $[\alpha]_D = +66.5°\ (c\ 26.0, H_2O)$.

4.37

a)

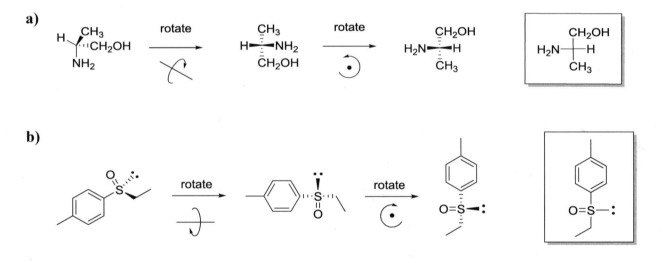

b)

c)

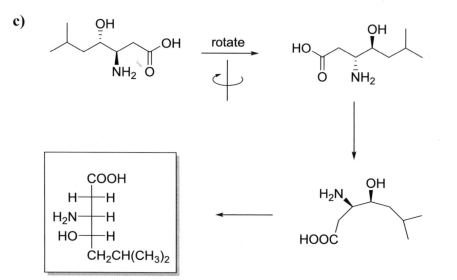

d)

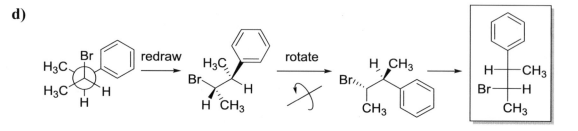

e)

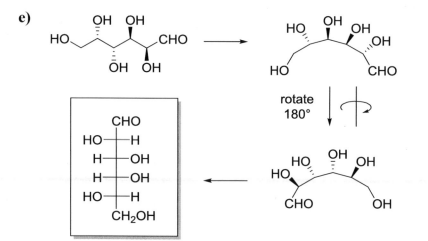

f)

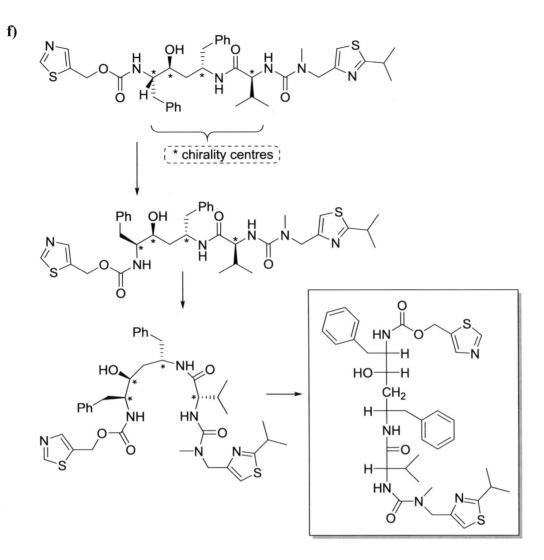

* chirality centres

4.39

a)

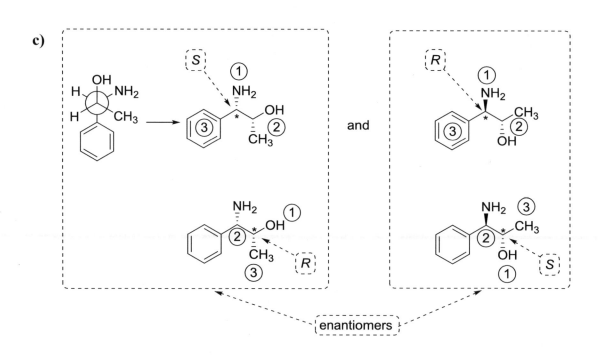

constitutional isomers

and

b)

diastereomers

and

cis-1,3-dimethylcyclohexane

c)

S ① *R* ①

and

R *S*

enantiomers

d)

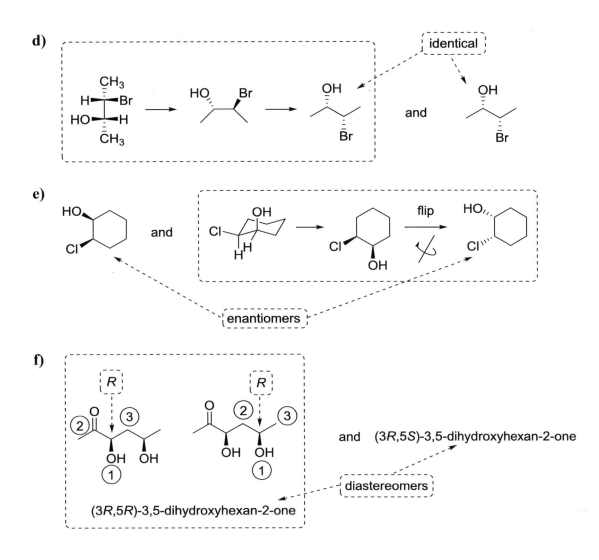

e)

f)

4.41

a) The 4 chirality centres will produce a maxiumum of 16 stereoisomers.

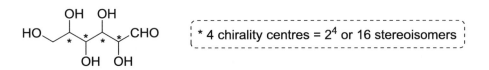

* 4 chirality centres = 2^4 or 16 stereoisomers

b) There are two chirality centres, which would produce four stereoisomers. The double bond could potentially show isomerism, but the *E* form would be highly strained and is unlikely to be formed.

* 2 chirality centres = 2^2 or 4 stereoisomers

c) The 4 chirality centres will produce a maximum of 16 stereoisomers.

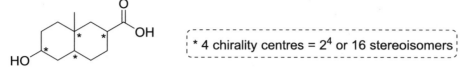

* 4 chirality centres = 2^4 or 16 stereoisomers

d) There are two chirality centres and one double bond, so a maxium of eight stereoisomers is possible.

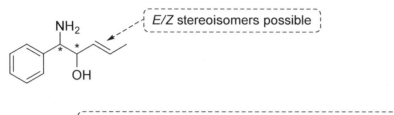

E/Z stereoisomers possible

* 2 chirality centres + 1 double bond = 2^3 or 8 stereoisomers

4.43

a) This is (2*R*,4*S*)-5-hydroxy-2,4-dimethylpentanoic acid.

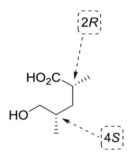

2*R*

4*S*

(2*R*,4*S*)-5-hydroxy-2,4-dimethylpentanoic acid

b) This is **not** (2*R*,4*S*)-5-hydroxy-2,4-dimethylpentanoic acid.

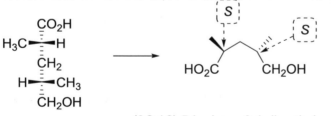

(2*S*,4*S*)-5-hydroxy-2,4-dimethylpentanoic acid

c) This is **not** (2*R*,4*S*)-5-hydroxy-2,4-dimethylpentanoic acid.

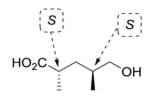

(2*S*,4*S*)-5-hydroxy-2,4-dimethylpentanoic acid

d) This is (2*R*,4*S*)-5-hydroxy-2,4-dimethylpentanoic acid.

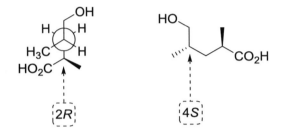

(2*R*,4*S*)-5-hydroxy-2,4-dimethylpentanoic acid

4.45

There would be 5 mmol – 1 mmol = 4 mmol of excess L-tartaric acid in a total of 6 mmol. The purity would be 4/6, or 67%.

4.47

In the Fischer projection of each amino acid, the highest oxidized group is placed in the top position and its side chain is placed in the bottom position.

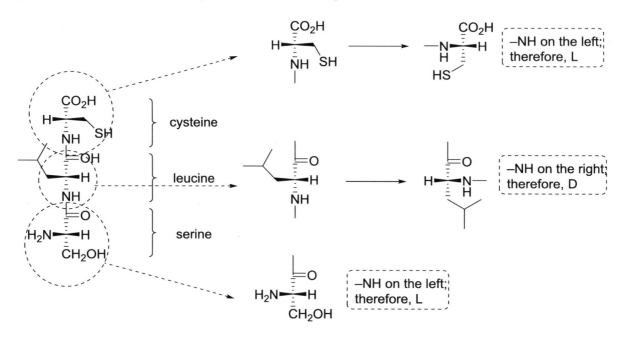

4.49

The possible isomers are:

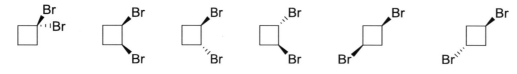

a) There are three unique constitutional isomers:

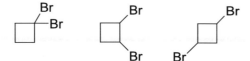

b) There is one pair of enantiomers:

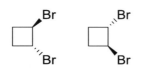

c) There are three pairs of diastereomers:

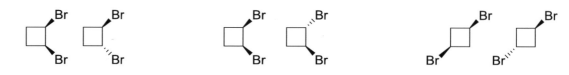

d) Four of the compounds are achiral:

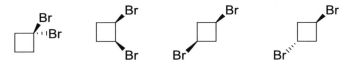

e) One of the achiral compounds is also a meso compound:

MCAT Style Problems

4.51

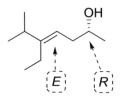

So, the answer would be (c): (*R*,*E*)-5-ethyl-6-methylhept-4-en-2-ol.

4.53

Since we are only looking for %ee, ratios of volumes will be equivalent to ratios of concentration. The lost solution will have the same composition as the remaining solution (enantiomers will have the same vapour pressure), so the remaining 6 mL of solution will still have the same 3:2 mixture of (*R*) and (*S*) as the original 10 mL solution. Using the amounts in the original solution to simplify the math:

Net excess of (*R*): 6 mL (*R*) – 4 mL (*S*) = 2 mL excess pure (*R*)

$$\%ee = \frac{\text{excess amount}}{\text{total amount}} \times 100\% = \frac{2 \text{ mL}}{10 \text{ mL}} \times 100\% = 20\%$$

So, the expected rotation would be 20% of that of pure (*R*), which would be $0.20 \times -13.5°$, or $-2.7°$.

So, the correct answer is (d).

Challenge Problems

4.55

a) A chiral carbon with four different substituents using only carbon and hydrogen is needed. Starting with a central carbon and adding successively larger groups would lead to the simplest chiral alkane.

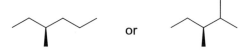

(or their enantiomers)

b) The smallest cycloalkane would be cyclopropane. Adding one methyl group does not give a chiral carbon, but adding a second does give this possibility.

   (or its enantiomer)

c) Three chiral cycloalkenes that contain only five carbon atoms are shown below.

(or their enantiomers)

4.56

As drawn below using wedges and dashes to better depict their three-dimensional structures, both *trans*-cyclooctene and *trans*-cyclodecene are chiral—their mirror images are not superposable onto their original structures. Each original and its mirror image are enantiomers. The difference between the enantiomers, as shown below for *trans*-cyclodecene, is which side of the double bond the rest of the ring lies on.

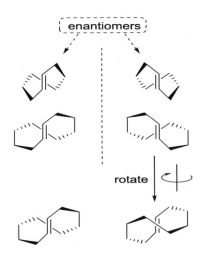

Trans-cyclodecene does not rotate plane-polarized light because there are equal amounts of its two enantiomers. Even a pure sample of one enantiomer of *trans*-cyclodecene will racemize; that is, it will eventually convert to equal amounts of enantiomers. It can do this because there are enough carbon atoms in the ring of *trans*-cyclodecene for those on one side of the double bond to readily swing around to the other side of the double bond by rotations around its single bonds, as shown below.

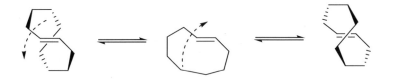

This rotation, however, is only possible with the larger cyclodecene; the ring in *trans*-cyclooctene is too small to get from one side of the double bond to the other. This restricted rotation means that enantiopure samples of *trans*-cyclooctene can be isolated and can be expected to rotate plane-polarized light. In contrast, it's not possible to isolate an enantiopure sample of *trans*-cyclodecene, since the rotations around its single bonds will quickly racemize the sample. Therefore, samples of *trans*-cyclodecene will not rotate plane-polarized light.

Chapter 5
Organic Reaction Mechanisms:
Using Curved Arrows to Analyze Reaction Mechanisms

PROBLEMS

5.15

Answers to (a) through (h) are labelled in the diagram below.

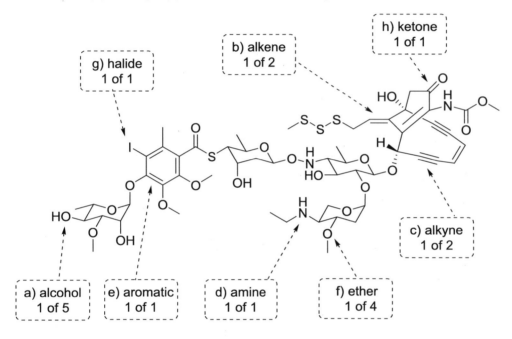

5.17

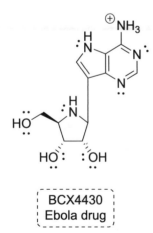

BCX4430
Ebola drug

5.19

a)

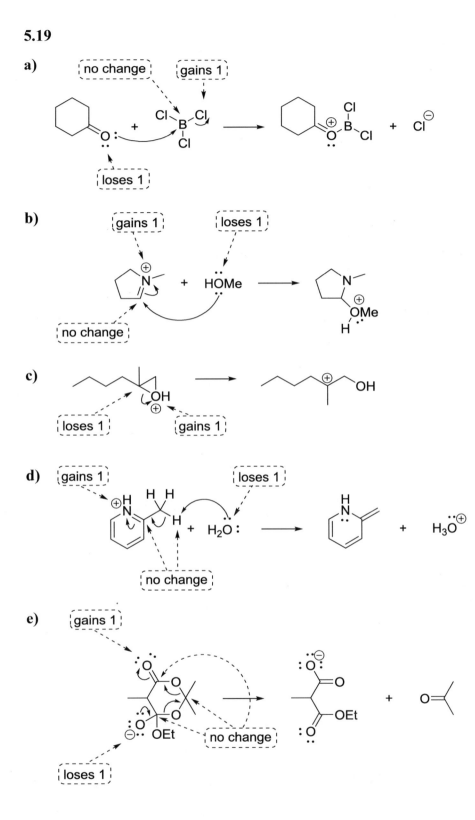

b)

c)

d)

e)

5.21

a)

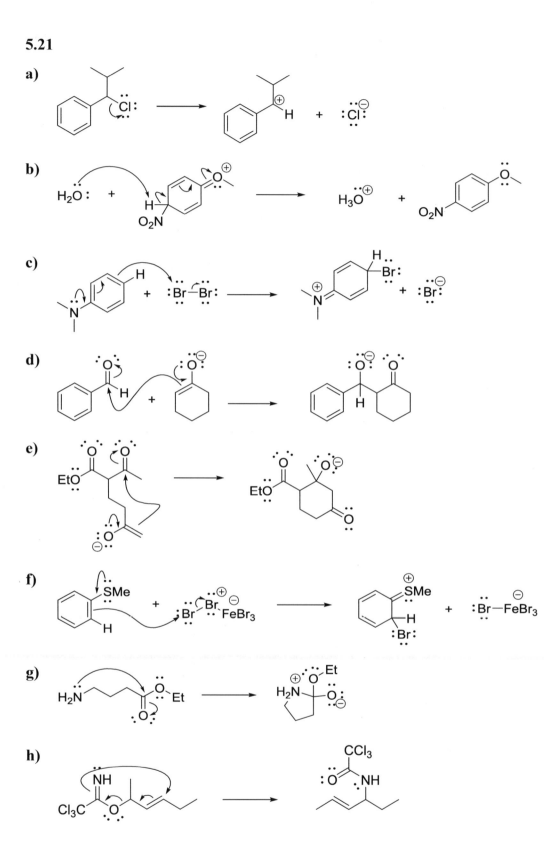

b)

c)

d)

e)

f)

g)

h)

5.23

a)

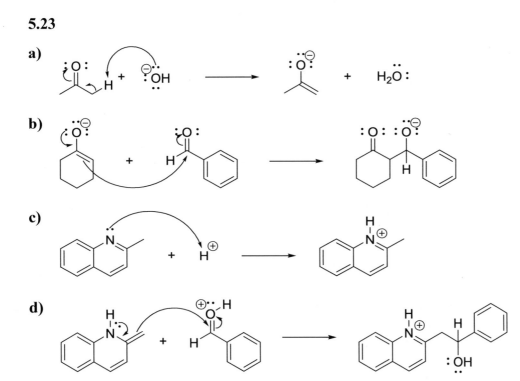

b)

c)

d)

5.25

The diagram below shows the missing curved arrows, lone pairs, and formal charges for the reactions. As well, the steps have been classified as intra- or intermolecular.

STEP 1: Intermolecular

STEP 2: Intramolecular

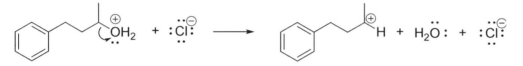

STEP 3: Intramolecular

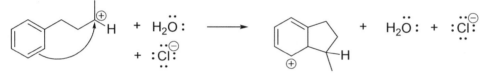

STEP 4: Intermolecular

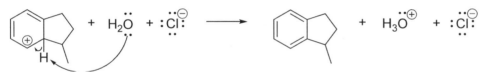

5.27

a) The H–Cl bond electrons need to move to the Cl atom to produce a chloride ion. This has been fixed below.

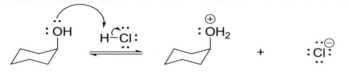

b) The added sidechain should have a charge, since it has contributed both electrons in the new bond. This is fixed in the diagram below.

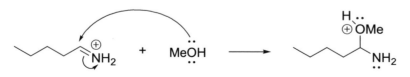

c) The C–H bond electrons form a new C–C bond and a new H–Cl bond is formed with a lone pair of electrons from the chlorine atom. The correct reaction is shown below.

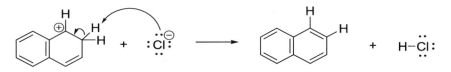

d) The reaction arrow is drawn backward. The electron flow is from the double bond to the incoming $H^{\oplus}$. This is corrected below.

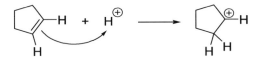

e) The new bond is formed between the carbonyl carbon and the incoming hydroxide ion, not with the carbonyl oxygen atom. Corrected below.

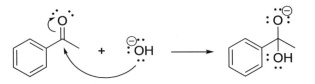

f) The flow of electrons was reversed. The arrows are correctly redrawn below.

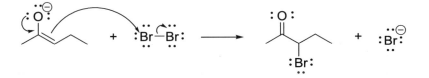

5.29

a) Two structures expected

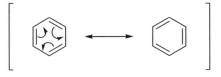

b) Five structures expected

c) Four structures expected

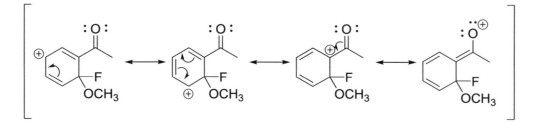

d) Seven structures expected

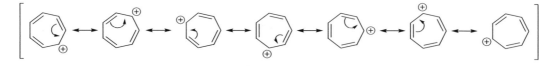

e) Four structures expected

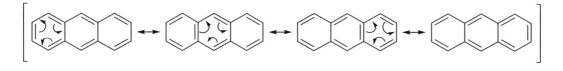

5.31

a) Resonance forms having atoms with all valence orbitals filled will contribute more to the resonance hybrid than those in which atoms have an empty orbital.

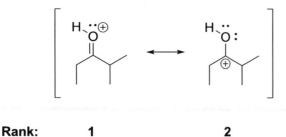

Rank: 1   2

b) The resonance form with the negative formal charge on the electronegative nitrogen atom is a greater contributor than the one with the negative charge on carbon.

$$\left[\; H_2C=\overset{\oplus}{N}=\overset{\ominus}{N}: \quad \longleftrightarrow \quad H_2\overset{\ominus}{C}-\overset{\oplus}{N}\equiv N: \; \right]$$

Rank: 1   2

c) The most important resonance form has no charges. The second most important has all orbitals filled with the negative charge on O. The third has all orbitals filled with the negative charge on C. The least important resonance form has an empty orbital on the C atom.

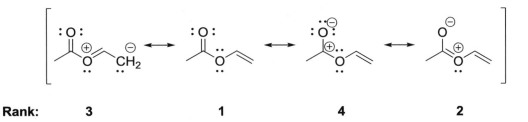

Rank: 3   1   4   2

d) The most important resonance form has no charges. The second most important has all orbitals filled. Both the third most important and the least important have an empty orbital on a C atom. The least important has the positive formal charge on the carbon atom adjacent to the negative formal charge.

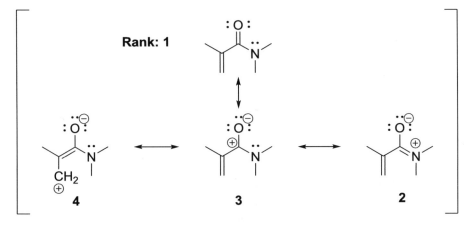

e) All structures are identical and therefore equally ranked.

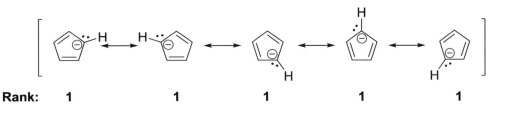

Rank: 1   1   1   1   1

f) There are three resonance forms that are equally the most important contributors. They are equal because they differ only in the position of the C=N π bond. They are the most important because all valence orbitals are filled. The remaining resonance form is least important because it has an empty orbital on the C atom.

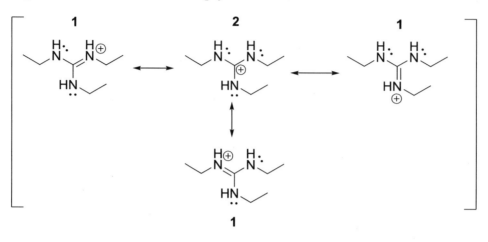

g) The most important resonance forms have the least number of formal charges. The positive formal charge in the ring of the second most important resonance form has greater separation from the positive formal charge on the $-NO_2$ nitrogen atom than in the two equivalent least important resonance forms.

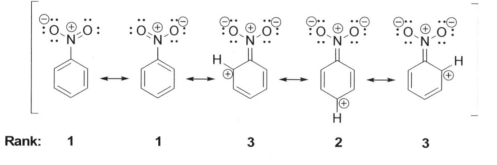

Rank: 1   1   3   2   3

5.33

a)

   or

The circled structure would be more stable, as it is capable of delocalizing the positive charge via resonance.

b)

 or

The circled structure is more stable, as it has available resonance forms. The charge on the other is isolated from the double bond by a saturated CH_2 group.

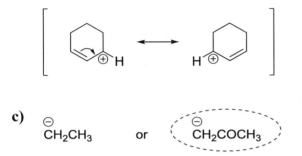

c)

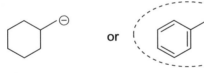

The circled structure would be more stable, since the negative charge is delocalized by resonance.

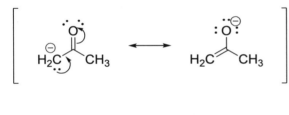

d)

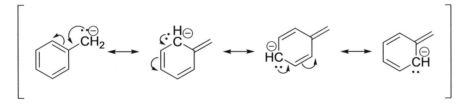 or

The negative charge in the circled structure is extensively delocalized, making it the most stable ion.

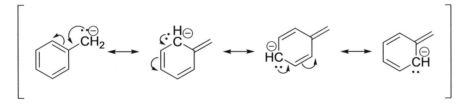

5.35

There are three different groupings based on similar resonance patterns.

<u>Group 1</u>

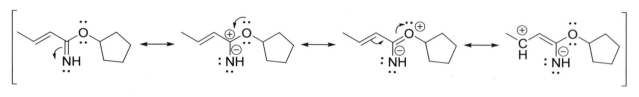

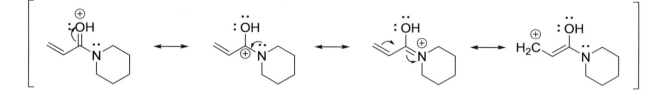

<u>Group 2</u>

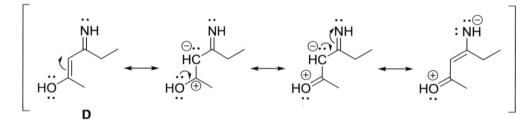

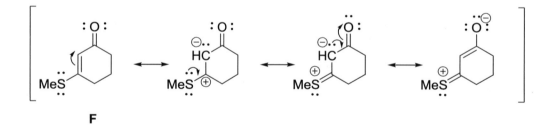

Group 3

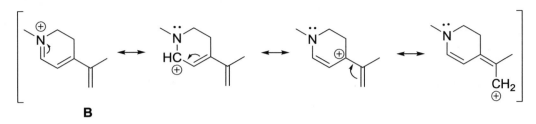

B

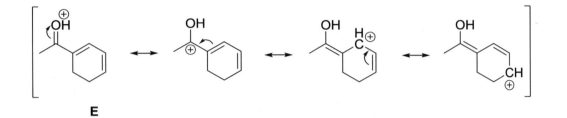

E

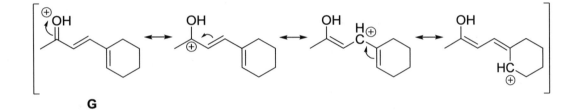

G

5.37

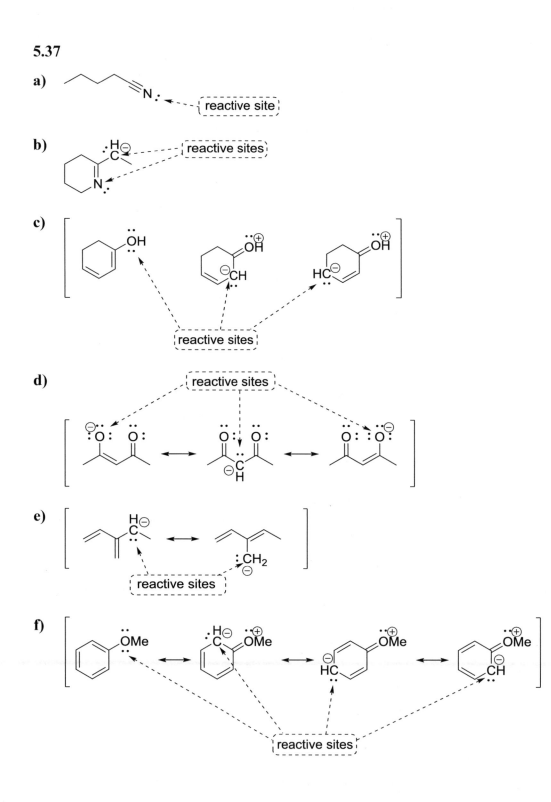

MCAT Style Problems

5.39

There are 10 lone pairs, or 20 nonbonding electrons. The correct answer is (d).

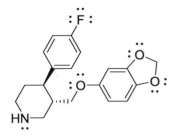

5.41

The answer is (b). There are three resonance structures, shown below.

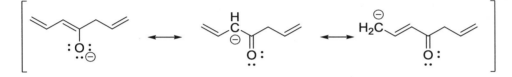

Challenge Problem

5.43

a) The resonance form **D** is not possible. The p orbitals are constrained by the rigid ring structure and cannot align to overlap and form a π bond with the adjacent C atom.

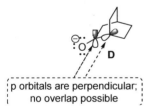

b) Similar to part (a). The lone pair on the N atom sits in an sp^2 hybridized orbital that lies perpendicular to the p orbitals of the ring, so overlap with them to establish π bonding is not possible. The lone p orbital on N that can form π bonds with the ring carbon atoms is already doing so.

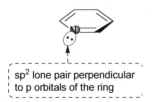

Chapter 6
Acids and Bases

PROBLEMS

6.15

a)

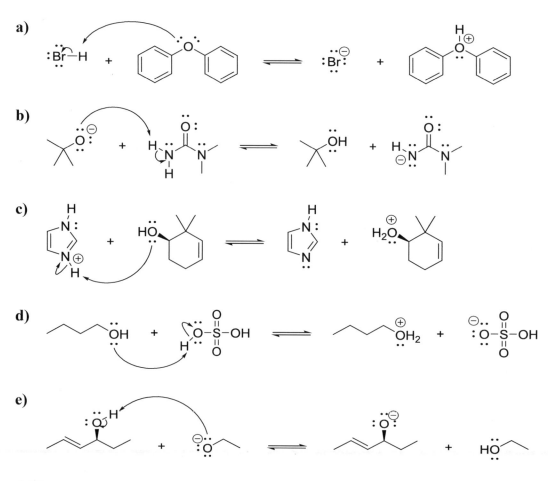

b)

c)

d)

e)

6.17

The energy diagram corresponds to an equilibrium, which favours the products over the reactants. Of the three equations, equation 2 favours the formation of the products since it is the only one where the conjugate acid (**HB**) is weaker (has a higher pK_a) than the acid.

6.19

a)

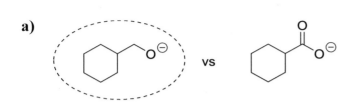

The bases are both charged; therefore, they can be compared directly. The negative charge is more stable on the carboxylate (right) since it is stabilized by resonance.

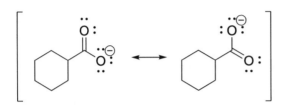

Therefore, the carboxylate is the weaker base and the deprotonated alcohol (left) is the stronger base.

b)

Compare the charged bases directly.

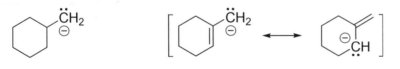

Base 1   **Base 2**

We can see that the negative charge is more stable in **Base 2** due to resonance stabilization. Therefore, the deprotonated alkane (**Base 1**) is the stronger base.

c)

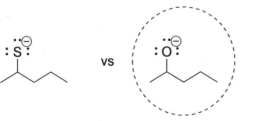

Negative charge is less stabilized in the deprotonated alcohol (right) since it is on a smaller atom (O versus S). Therefore, the deprotonated alcohol is a stronger base than the deprotonated thiol.

d)

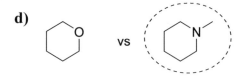

The bases are both neutral; therefore, the stability of their conjugate acids should be compared.

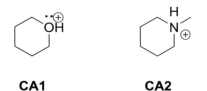

CA1   **CA2**

The positive charge is more stable on the less electronegative N atom; therefore, **CA2** is more stable than **CA1**. Since **CA2** is more stable, it is also a weaker acid, making its conjugate base—the amine—the stronger base.

e)

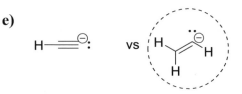

Comparing the charged bases directly, the negative charge is less stable in an sp^2 orbital on the deprotonated alkene (right) than in an sp orbital on the deprotonated alkyne (left). So, the deprotonated alkene is the stronger base.

f)

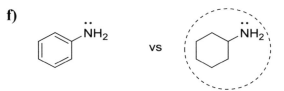

Cyclohexamine (right) has no contributing resonance forms, so its lone pair is localized on the nitrogen atom and easily protonated in an acid–base reaction. The lone pair in aniline is actually delocalized over multiple centres throughout the molecule, as shown in its resonance forms below. Protonation of the nitrogen centre will disrupt most of the resonance stabilization of the molecule. The lone pair of aniline is, therefore, not particularly basic.

g)

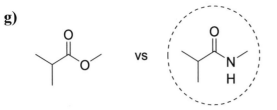

The charged conjugate acids need to be compared.

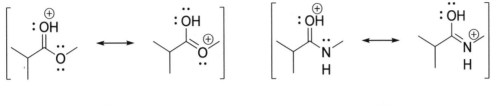

CA1   **CA2**

Both conjugate acids are resonance stabilized, but the positive charge on **CA2** is more stable since the positive charge is spread out over a less electronegative N atom. Since **CA2** is more stable, the amide (right) is the stronger base.

h)

These neutral bases need to be compared through their charged conjugate acids.

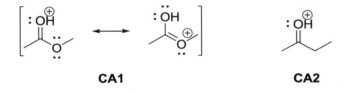

CA1   **CA2**

The positive charge on **CA1** is stabilized through resonance, so it is the more stable conjugate acid. Therefore, the ester (left) is more basic.

6.21

a) These are charged and their relative stabilities can be compared directly.

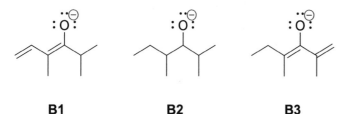

B1   **B2**   **B3**

Compound **B2** has no resonance stabilization, while both **B1** and **B3** have resonance forms.

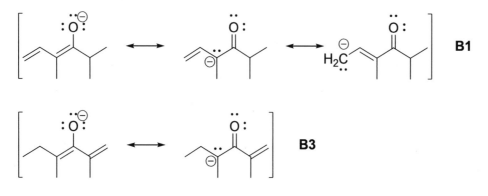

This would make **B2** the least stable base. **B1** has the negative charge delocalized over three atoms, while **B3** only uses two atoms; so, **B1** would be more stable than **B3**. Stability decreases base strength. So, the compounds in order of increasing basicity would be

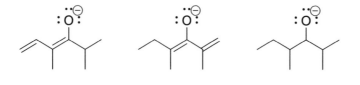

least basic   most basic

b) These are charged and their relative stabilities can be compared directly.

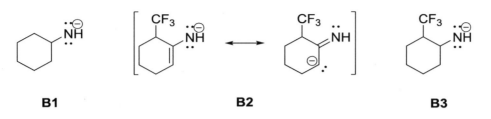

Both **B2** and **B3** have electron-withdrawing groups (–CF₃) near the negative charge, while **B1** does not. This stabilizes the negative charges on **B2** and **B**; so, **B1** is the least stable base. **B2** also has resonance forms, which delocalize the charge onto two atoms. So, **B2** would be more stable than **B3**. Since base strength decreases with increasing stability, the compounds in order of increasing basicity would be

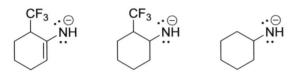

least basic   most basic

c) All are charged species and their relative stabilities can be compared directly.

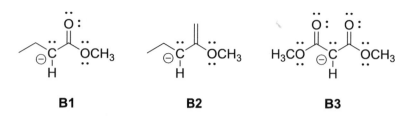

B1   **B2**   **B3**

All three are resonance stabilized.

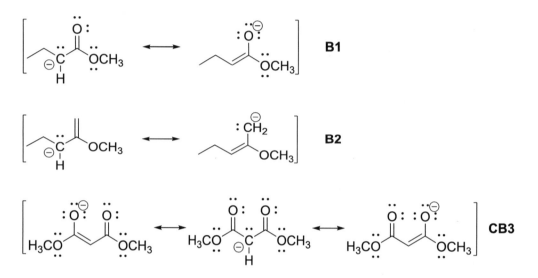

B1

B2

CB3

B3 would be the most stable since it delocalizes the charge over three atoms, two of which are more electronegative oxygen atoms. **B2** and **B1** delocalize the charge over two atoms but, in **B1**, one is an oxygen, versus a carbon in **B2**. This would make **B1** the more stable of the two molecules. The relative stabilities would then be **B2, B1, B3** (most stable), and the ranking of molecules from least basic to most basic is

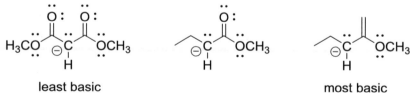

least basic   most basic

d) These are easily compared by looking at the conjugate acids of each base.

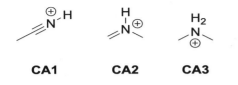

CA1   **CA2**   **CA3**

The difference between these is the hybridization of the orbital that has the lone pair once the proton of the above conjugate acids is removed. In **CA1**, the resulting lone pair would be in an sp hybrid orbital on N. The lone pair is in an sp^2 hybrid in **B2** and in an sp^3 hybrid in **B3**. The lone pair in the sp hybrid will be lowest in energy followed by the sp^2 hybrid. The lone pair in the sp^3 hybrid will be the highest in energy. Since lower energy is equivalent to a more stable base, the ordering from least basic to most basic would be

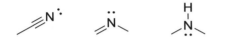

least basic   **most basic**

e) These are most easily compared by looking at their conjugate acids.

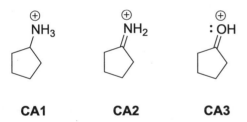

CA1   **CA2**   **CA3**

Once again, the difference between these is the hybridization of the orbital that each conjugate acid uses to bond with the proton. In **CA1**, it is an sp^3-hybridized orbital (which has the least s character) on nitrogen. In **CA2** and **CA3**, it is an sp^2 orbital (of greater s character) on N and O respectively. **CA1** will be the most stable conjugate acid since the charge is in a hybrid orbital having less s character, keeping it further from the positively charged nucleus. In **CA2** and **CA3**, the positive charge would be more stable on the relatively more electropositive nitrogen atom. So, **CA2** should be more stable than **CA3**. A more stable conjugate acid is weaker and, therefore, its base form should be a stronger base. The order of basicity from weakest to strongest is then

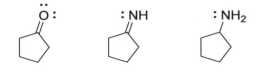

least basic   **most basic**

f) These are not charged and their charged conjugate acids should be compared.

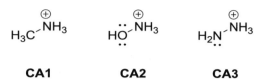

CA1   **CA2**   **CA3**

The substituents have different inductive effects on the positive charge in each of these conjugate acids. The methyl group in **CA1** is electron donating and would stabilize the positive charge. The hydroxyl and amino groups in **CA2** and **CA3** respectively are electron withdrawing and would destabilize the positive charge. **CA1** would be the most stable conjugate acid. Since oxygen is more electronegative than nitrogen, it is more effective at withdrawing charge, and **CA2** should be less stable than **CA3**. So, the conjugate acids in order of increasing stability are **CA2** (least stable), **CA3, CA1** (most stable). Basicity is inversely related to conjugate acid strength, so the bases in order of increasing basicity would be

HO–NH₂   H₂N–NH₂   H₃C–NH₂

least basic   most basic

6.23

a) Reactants

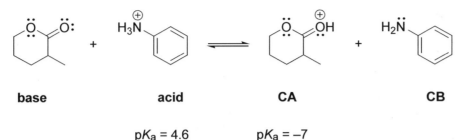

base   **acid**   **CA**   **CB**

$pK_a = 4.6$ $pK_a = -7$

The strongest acid is the conjugate acid **CA** so the **reactants** should be favoured.

b) Products

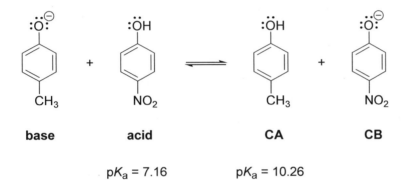

base   **acid**   **CA**   **CB**

$pK_a = 7.16$ $pK_a = 10.26$

The **acid** is stronger than **CA** in this case due to the electron withdrawal and resonance stabilization of its conjugate base **CB** provided by the NO_2 group. So, the reaction should favour the products.

c) Reactants

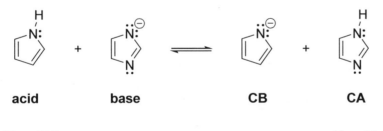

acid   **base**   **CB**   **CA**

$pK_a = 17.5$ $pK_a = 14.5$

Since the conjugate acid **CA** is the stronger of the two acids, the reactants should be favoured.

d) Reactants

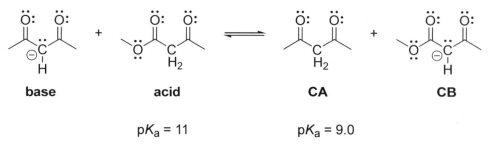

base   **acid**   **CA**   **CB**

$pK_a = 11$ $pK_a = 9.0$

The conjugate acid **CA** is the stronger acid, so the reactants are favoured.

e) Products

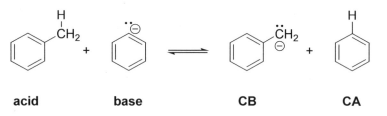

acid   **base**   **CB**   **CA**

$pK_a = 41$ $pK_a = 43$

The **acid** is stronger than the conjugate acid **CA** in this case, so the products are favoured.

f) Reactants

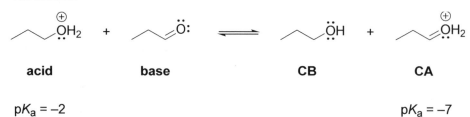

acid   **base**   **CB**   **CA**

$pK_a = -2$ $pK_a = -7$

The conjugate acid **CA** is a stronger acid than the acid on the left, so the reactants are favoured.

6.25

a) The overall reaction is

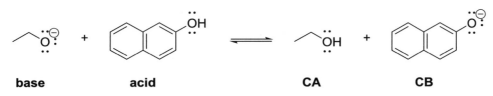

base **acid** **CA** **CB**

To determine the direction of the equilibrium, the charged species are compared. For this reaction, that means comparing the **base** and the conjugate base (**CB**). The conjugate base can participate in resonance with the neighbouring π bonds, while the reactant base has no resonance. Therefore, the conjugate base is more stable, meaning it is the weaker base. Therefore, the equilibrium will favour the products since equilibria favour formation of the weaker species.

b) The overall reaction is

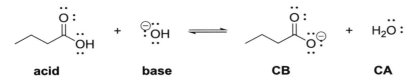

acid **base** **CB** **CA**

Comparing the charged species (**base** and **CB**), the conjugate base **CB** would be more stable since the negative charge on the oxygen is stabilized by resonance. So the **CB** is the weaker base and the reaction would favour products.

c) The overall reaction is

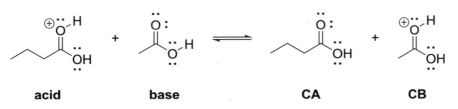

acid **base** **CA** **CB**

The **acid** and **CA** have identical structural features near the positive charge. They should have very similar stabilities and, therefore, similar acid strengths. Neither reactants nor products would be favoured.

d) First, it must be established which reactant will act as the acid and which will be the base. Comparing their respective conjugate bases, **CB1** is resonance stabilized while **CB2** is not.

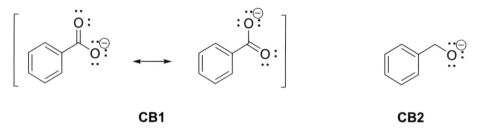

CB1   **CB2**

CB1 is, therefore, more stable, so its conjugate acid—the reactant on the left—is more acidic than the reactant on the right. The reactant on the right must act as the base. The overall reaction is

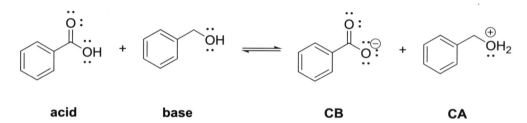

acid   **base**   **CB**   **CA**

The **CB** and **CA** are both charged, while the **acid** and **base** are both neutral. Therefore, the **CA** and **CB** would be expected to be the stronger acid and base respectively. So, the reactants are favoured.

e) The overall reaction is

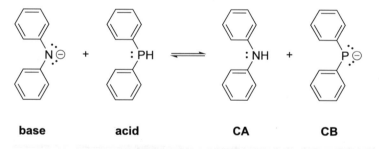

base   **acid**   **CA**   **CB**

Both the **base** and **CB** are charged and so will be compared. The negative charge in both is resonance stabilized with the aromatic rings, but this effect should be similar in both cases. The charge is more stable in the **CB** versus the **base** since the phosphorus is larger and can disperse the negative charge over a larger volume. So, the **CB** is weaker than the **base** and the products would be favoured.

f) The overall reaction is

acid   **base**   **CB**   **CA**

The **CB** would be more stable than the **base**, since the fluorine atoms are closer to the negative charge in the **CB** and stabilize it by induction. So, the **CB** would be the weaker of the two bases and the products would be favoured.

g) The overall reaction is

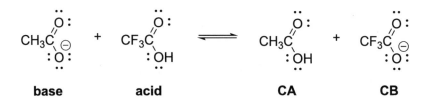

base   **acid**   **CA**   **CB**

Both the **base** and **CB** have resonance-stabilized carboxylate groups. But the charge would be more stable in the **CB** because the CF_3 group would inductively remove electron density, stabilizing the charge, while the CH_3 group is an electron donor and would destabilize the charge. So, the **CB** is the most stable and the products would be favoured in this reaction.

h) The overall reaction is

CCl$_3$ÖH   +   CF$_3$Ö⁻   ⇌   CCl$_3$Ö⁻   +   CF$_3$ÖH

acid   **base**   **CB**   **CA**

The negative charge would be more stable in the **base** than in the **CB**, with the fluorines more effectively removing electron density through induction than chlorines. The **base** would be most stable and the reactants favoured.

6.27

a) To evaluate the acidity of the three types of protons, compare their corresponding conjugate bases.

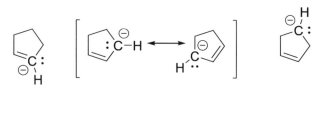

CB-A   **CB-B**   **CB-C**

CB-B is the most stable since it is the only one stabilized by resonance. Between **CB-A** and **CB-C**, **CB-A** is more stable since its negative charge is associated with an sp^2-hybridized orbital, which has greater s character than the sp^3 orbital in **CB-C**. Therefore, the conjugate bases can be ranked as follows: **CB-C**, **CB-A**, **CB-B**, where **CB-B** is the most stable. The more stable a conjugate base is, the weaker a base it is and the stronger its corresponding acid is. Therefore, the ranking of increasing proton acidity in the original molecule is **C, A, B**.

b) The conjugate bases formed by removing each of these protons are shown below.

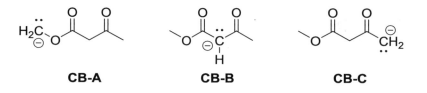

CB-A   **CB-B**   **CB-C**

CB-A has no resonance stabilization while **CB-B** and **CB-C** both do. **CB-A** is the least stable conjugate base. **CB-B** can delocalize the negative charge onto both carbonyl oxygens, while **CB-C** can only delocalize onto one carbonyl oxygen. **CB-B** would be more stable than **CB-C**. The conjugate bases would be ranked **CB-A** (least stable, most basic), **CB-C**, **CB-B** (most stable, least basic). The rank of increasing acidity in the original molecule will, therefore, be **A** (least acidic), **C**, **B** (most acidic).

c) To compare acidity, we can consider the conjugate bases formed from deprotonating each of these sites.

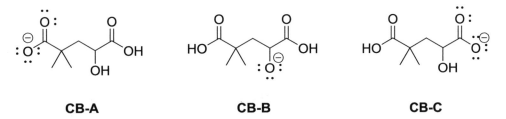

CB-A   **CB-B**   **CB-C**

CB-B has no resonance stabilization while **CB-A** and **CB-C** both have resonance-stabilized carboxylate groups. **CB-B** is the least stable conjugate base. **CB-A** and **CB-C** have similar delocalization, but **CB-A** has two adjacent methyl groups, which inductively destabilize the negative charge, while the oxygen atom of the nearby OH group in **CB-C** would inductively stabilize its negative charge. The conjugate bases would be ranked **CB-C** (most stable), **CB-A**, **CB-B** (least stable), and the acid ranking of the protons in the original molecule will be **B** (least acidic), **A**, **C** (most acidic).

d) Consider the charged conjugate bases for each of these sites.

CB-A   **CB-B**

Both conjugate bases will have resonance structures, but **CB-B** will have three resonance forms while **CB-A** has only two resonance forms. So, **CB-B** will be more stable and the rank of increasing acidity of the indicated protons in the molecule will be **A** (least acidic), **B** (most acidic).

e) The two charged conjugate bases formed by deprotonation at each of these sites are

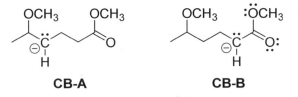

CB-A   **CB-B**

CB-A has no resonance stabilization while **CB-B** has two resonance forms, which delocalize its negative charge. So, **CB-B** is more stable than **CB-A** and the sites of acidity would be ranked **A** (least acidic), **B** (most acidic).

f) The three conjugate bases to consider would be

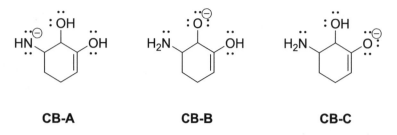

CB-A   **CB-B**   **CB-C**

CB-A would be the least stable, with the positive charge on the nitrogen, while both **CB-B** and **CB-C** have the negative charge on the more electronegative oxygen atom. **CB-C** is resonance stabilized by the C–C double bond while **CB-B** is not, making **CB-C** the more stable of the two. The relative stability of the bases would be **CB-C** (most stable, least basic), **CB-B**, **CB-A** (least stable, most basic), and the relative site acidities in the original molecule would be **A** (least acidic), **B**, **C** (most acidic).

g) The conjugate bases that would form are

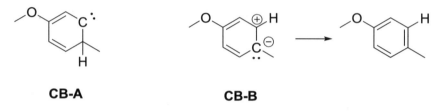

CB-A   **CB-B**

CB-A is very unstable, with a lone pair of electrons as well as an empty orbital on the carbon atom. **CB-B** would form a very stable aromatic ring, as shown. The acidity of the protons would be **A** (least acidic), **B** (most acidic).

h) Draw the resonance forms of the acid.

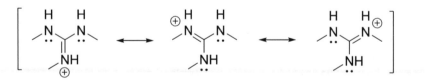

It can be seen that all of the nitrogen atoms in the molecule are equivalent. All three sites **A**, **B**, and **C** will, therefore, be equally acidic.

6.29

The reaction of a base with acetic acid can be represented by the following general equation:

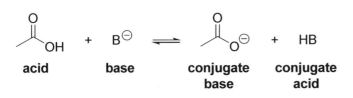

For the above equilibrium to favour the products, the conjugate acids formed as products must be weaker than the reactant acid, acetic acid (i.e., the pK_a of HB, the conjugate acid of the base, must be lower than 4.8, the pK_a of acetic acid). The conjugate acids of the five bases and their pK_a are

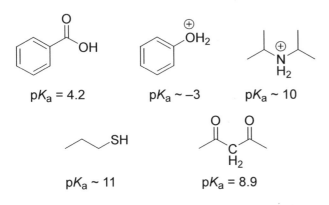

Therefore, the three bases that would react with acetic acid and favour the products at equilibrium are

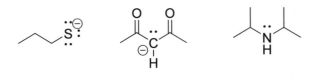

6.31

a) The four basic sites are indicated below.

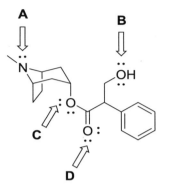

Protonating site **A** would put a positive charge on the less electronegative nitrogen while protonating the other sites would have a positive charge on an oxygen. Nitrogen would stabilize the positive charge best, so site **A** is most basic: **C, D, B, A** (most basic).

b) The two acidic sites are indicated below.

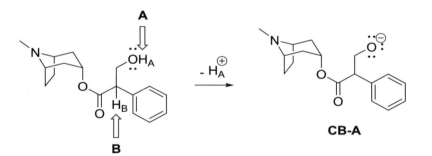

Deprotonation of site **A** would leave the negative charge on the electronegative oxygen in its conjugate base **CB-A**. Deprotonation of site **B** yields a conjugate base with multiple resonance forms.

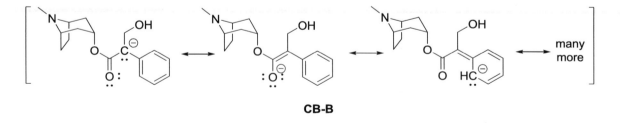

Most of these resonance forms have the negative charge on less electronegative carbon atoms. Only one resonance form has it on the carbonyl oxygen atom. As a result, **CB-A** will be more stable than **CB-B**. Site **A** will, therefore, be more acidic than site **B**.

6.33

Answer: (a).

First assign the **acid**, **base**, conjugate acid (**CA**), and conjugate base (**CB**).

Let's compare the four statements individually.

a) The equilibrium favours the products.

The **acid** is positively charged and the conjugate acid **CA** is negatively charged. The **acid** is a stronger acid than **CA**. The **base** is negatively charged and the **CB** is neutral, so the **base** is the strongest base. Either of these comparisons show this statement to be true.

b) Water is the conjugate acid.

As indicated above, this is false.

c) Bicarbonate is the conjugate base.

Again, this is false, as shown above.

d) Hydronium ion is a weak acid.

Hydronium ion is the result of the ionization of strong acids, so this is false.

So, statement (a) is the only true statement.

6.35

To evaluate the acidity of these neutral compounds, one needs to look at their conjugate bases. All four conjugate bases benefit from resonance stabilization; however, an important difference is seen when examining the resonance contributors, which move the charge into the substituent on the aromatic ring. Although such a resonance structure can be drawn for all four conjugate bases, the resonance contributor drawn for **CB-D** is not a valid contributor.

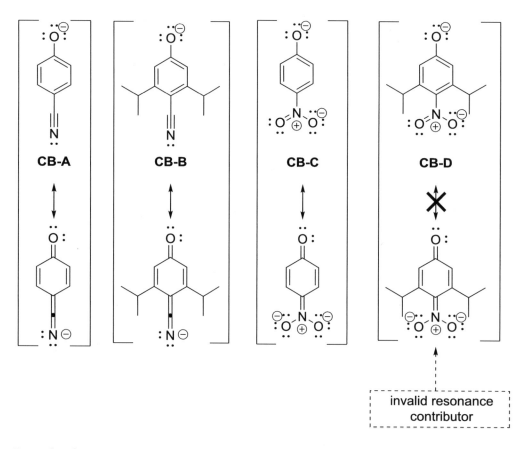

invalid resonance contributor

In order for resonance to exist, the p orbitals involved need to be parallel to each other in order to effectively overlap. Because of the bulky isopropyl groups on **CB-D**, the planar nitro group cannot lie in the plane of the ring; rather, it needs to rotate in order to avoid steric interactions with the isopropyl groups. This means its p orbitals are not lined up with the π system of the ring to achieve overlap, and resonance with the nitro group is not possible.

nitro group rotates to avoid steric strain with isopropyl groups

The resonance stabilization that **CB-D** should have from its electron-withdrawing nitro group is effectively lost. **CB-D** is, therefore, less stable than **CB-C** and, therefore, more basic. This, in turn, means compound **D** is a weaker acid than compound **C**.

The same situation does not exist for compounds **A** and **B** since the CN group is linear and steric interactions with the isopropyl groups will be (almost) absent.

Chapter 7
π Bonds as Electrophiles:
Reactions of Carbonyls and Related Functional Groups

PROBLEMS

7.21

a)

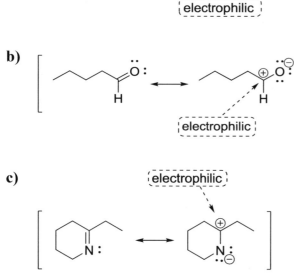

b)

c)

d) There is a positive charge in each resonance form, but having the charge on the more electropositive carbon makes that resonance form the more important one.

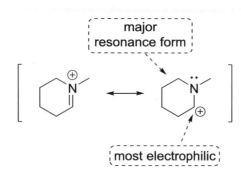

e)

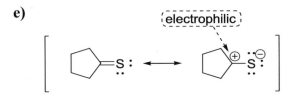

f) The more important resonance form has the positive charge on the carbon.

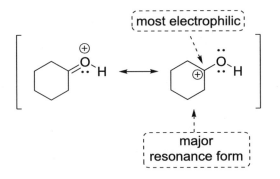

g) The more importatn resonance form has the positive charge on the carbon.

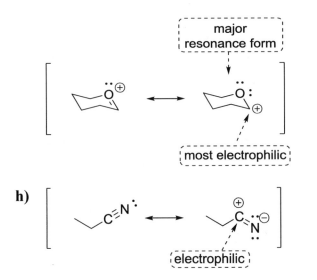

h)

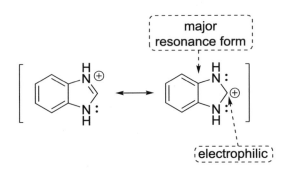

i) The more important resonance form has the positive charge on the carbon.

7.23

a)

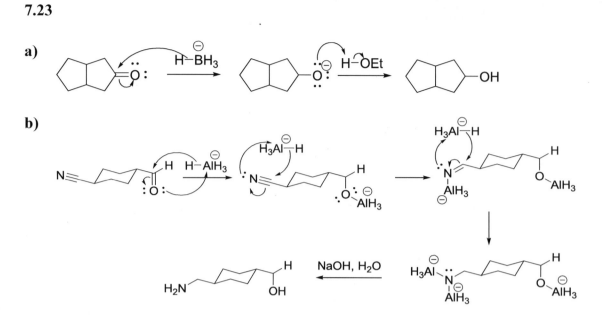

b)

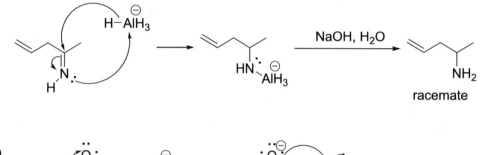

c) The C=C bond does not react with metal hydrides.

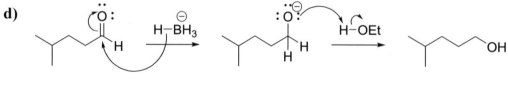

d)

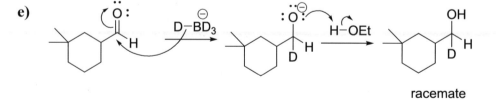

e)

7.25

a)

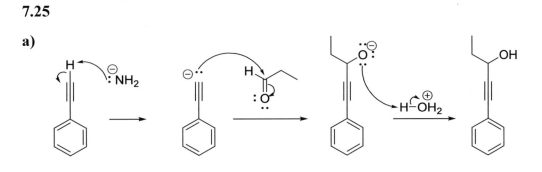

b)

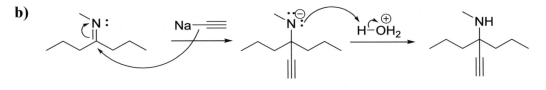

c)

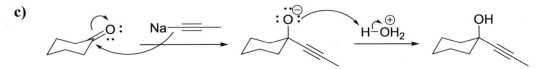

d)

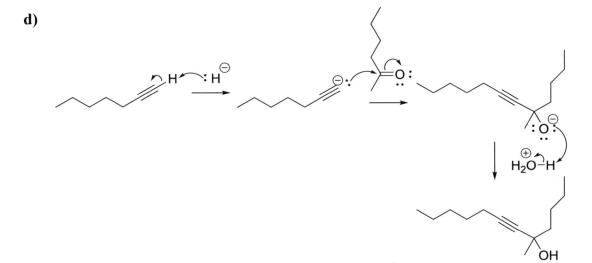

7.27

a)

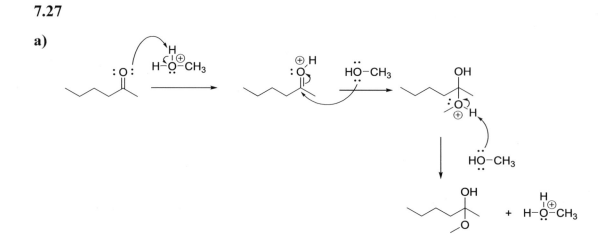

b)

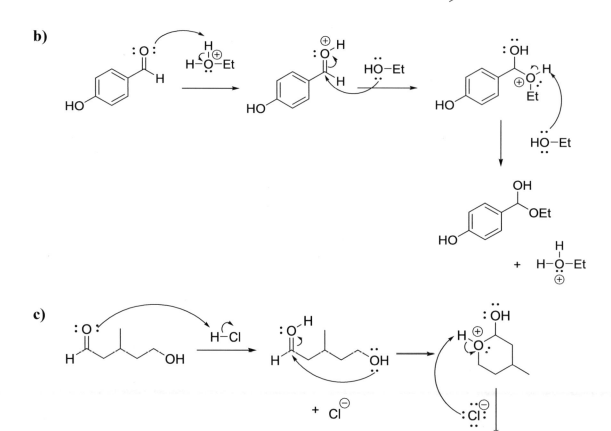

c)

d)

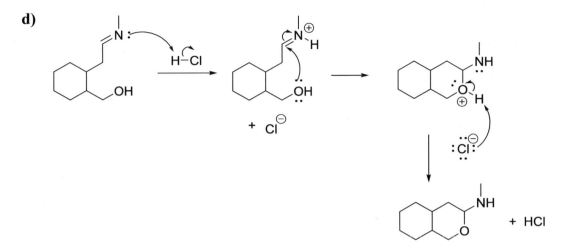

7.29

a)

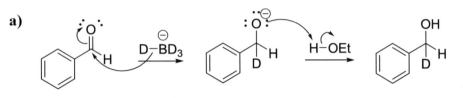

b)

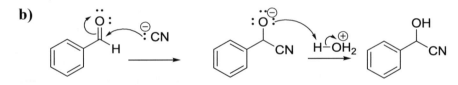

c)

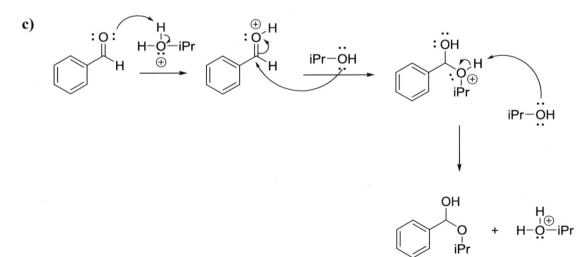

d)

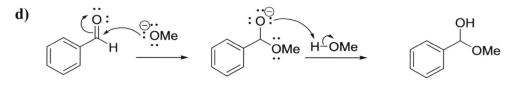

e)

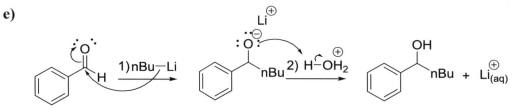

7.31

a) Acid catalyzed

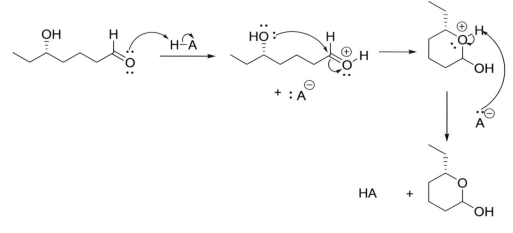

Base catalyzed

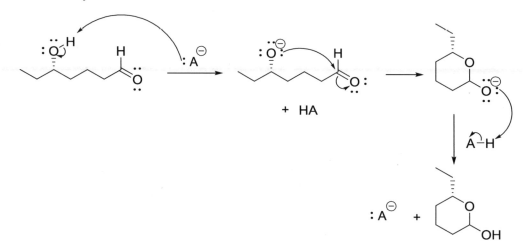

b), c)

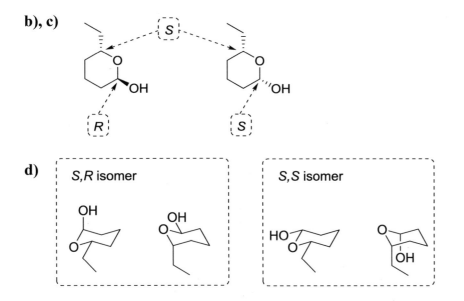

d)

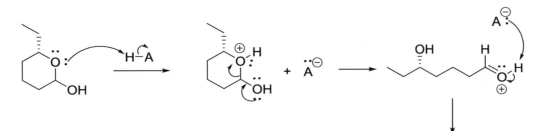

e) Acid catalyzed

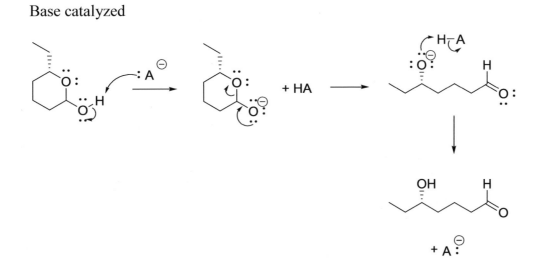

Base catalyzed

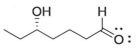

7.33

a) There is no difference in steric hindrance on the two faces of the aldehyde group, so the products are produced in equal amounts.

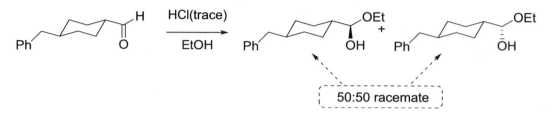

b) Approach of the Grignard would be inhibited on one face of the ketone by the large alkyl group. This would lead to an excess of the product from addition on the opposite face.

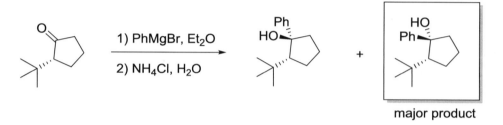

major product

c) Due to the symmetry of the molecule, addition on either face is equally likely and leads to the same stereoisomer.

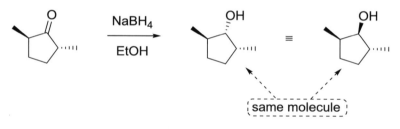

same molecule

d) The ring's isopropyl group makes the approach of the nucleophile from that face side less favourable. This leads to a preferred product, as shown.

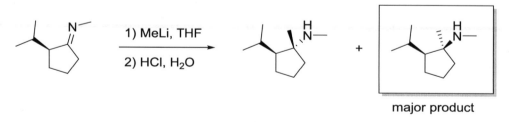

major product

e) There is no preferred side for the nucleophilic attack.

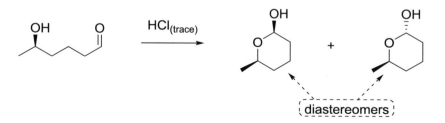

diastereomers

7.35

The reaction cannot be a simple nucleophilic substitution since that would produce the opposite stereochemistry at the bromine substituted carbon.

SN₂ reaction

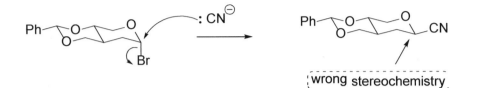

However, if a oxonium intermediate is formed, nucleophilic attack can occur at either face and produce some of the indicated product.

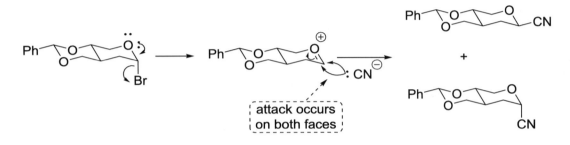

7.37

a) Acid catalysis

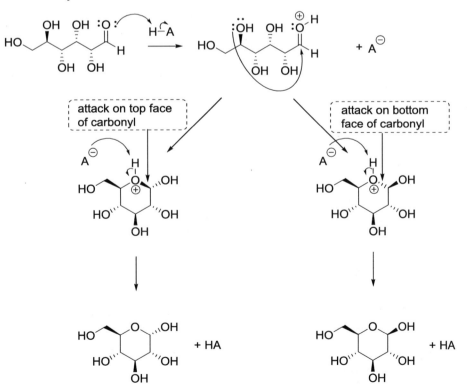

b) Base catalysis

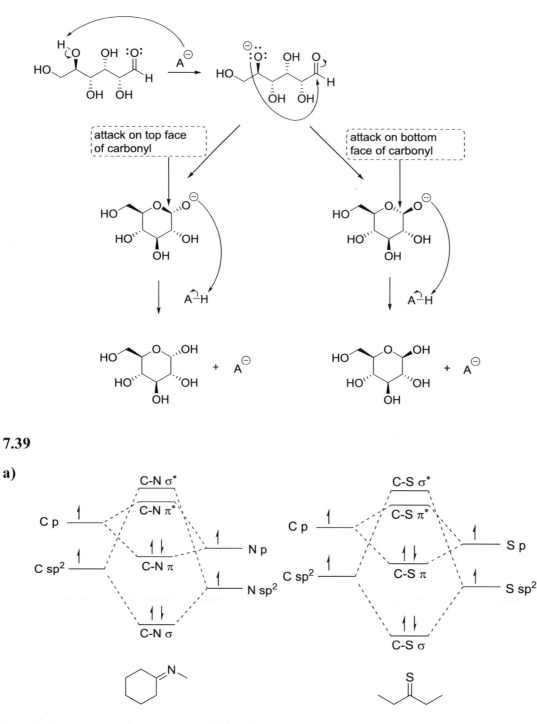

7.39

a)

b) In both cases, the LUMO will be the π* orbital.

c) Both LUMO's are closest in energy to the carbon p orbital energy. So, nucleophiles (electron donors) will be most likely to react at the carbon.

d) The HOMO's are both the filled π orbitals. They are closest in energy to N or S, respectively. So. electrophiles would react at the N or the S atoms.

7.41

a)

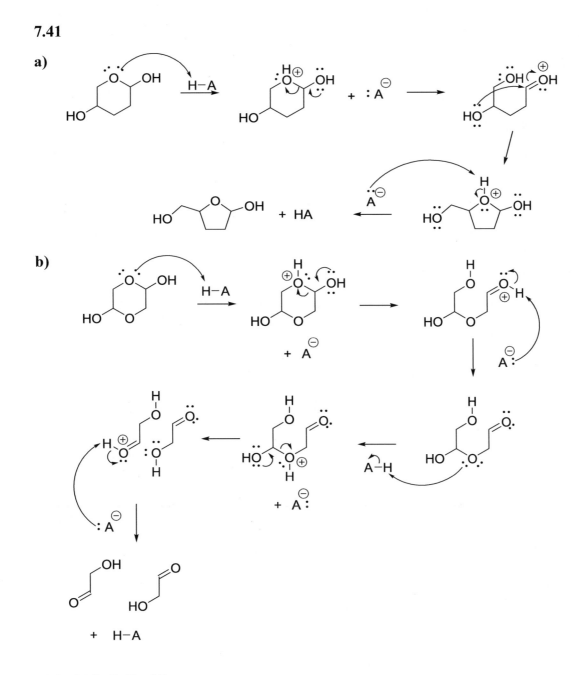

b)

MCAT Style Problems

7.43

Answer: (b).

Challenge Problem

7.45

a) Step 1

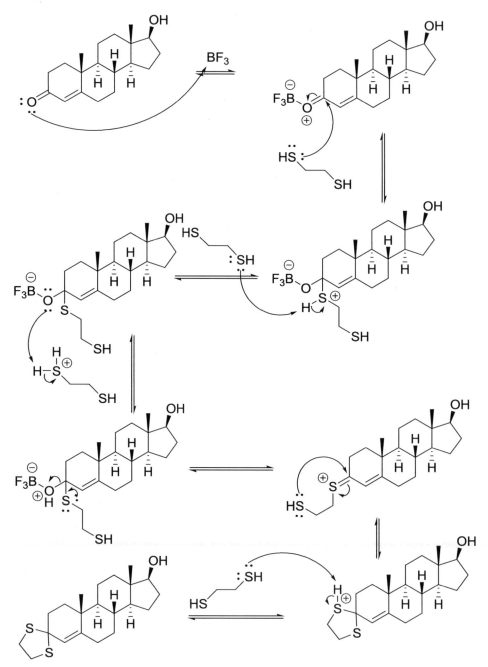

b) The third step is an oxidation (loss of two H) from an alcohol to a carbonyl. The fourth step is a reduction from a carbonyl to an alcohol. The second step is also a reduction.

c) Final step

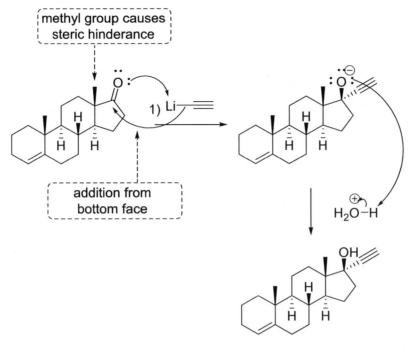

lynestrenol

Chapter 8
π Bonds as Nucleophiles:
Reactions of Alkenes, Alkynes, Dienes, and Enols

PROBLEMS

8.21

The pair of electrons was being equally shared by the two carbon atoms. In the product, one carbon is still sharing its electron in the carbon–electrophile bond (no change in charge). The other carbon has lost the electron it used to be sharing, so it has a +1 charge. As well, charge conservation still applies to organic reactions.

8.23

The reverse reaction would be thermodynamically unfavourable, since the products in the reverse reaction would be higher in energy than its reactants.

The rate-determining step would be the first step in the reverse reaction (second step in the forward reaction), as it has the highest activation energy barrier.

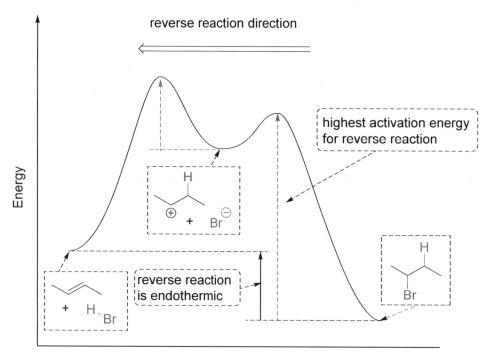

8.25

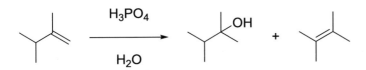

Both products form from the same carbocation.

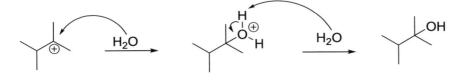

In one case, the carbocation reacts with water, acting as a nucleophile.

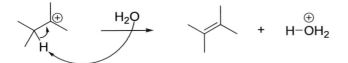

In the other case, water acts as a base to remove a proton.

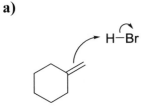

8.27

a)

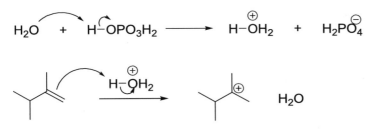

tertiary carbocation
(more stable)

Markovnikov product

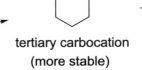

primary carbocation

b)

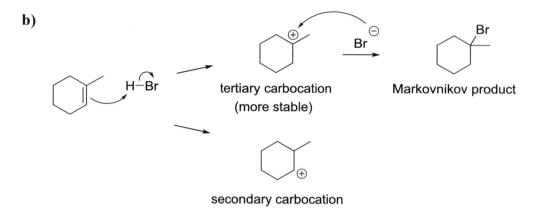

c) The alkene is symmetrical, so the two carbocation intermediates that form are indistinguishable and of identical energy. The product of each is the same.

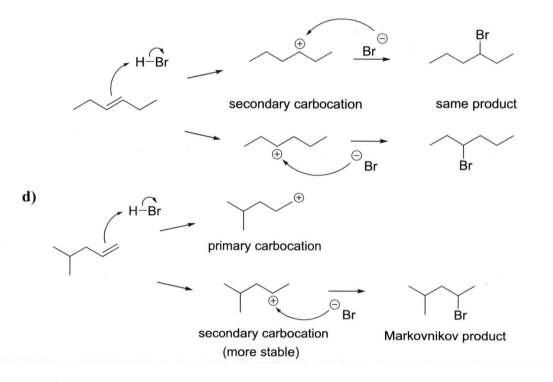

8.29

a) and **b)**

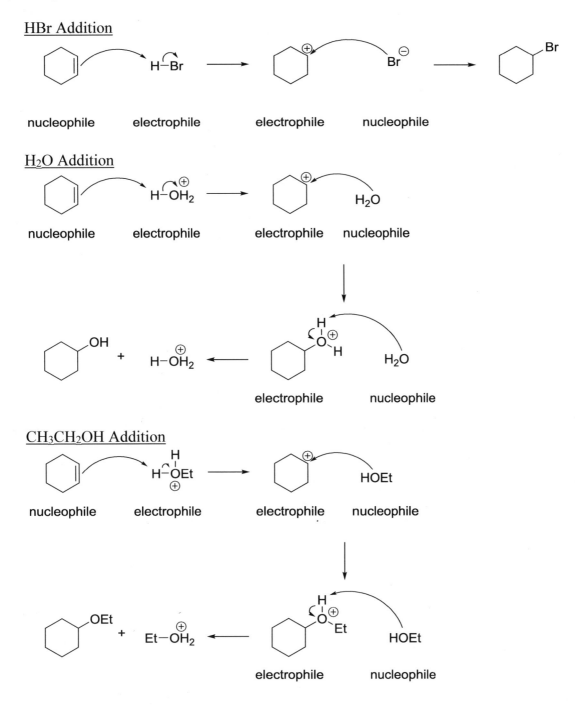

Underlined labels visible: HBr Addition, H₂O Addition, CH₃CH₂OH Addition

c) Acid is needed because water and alcohols are not acidic enough to protonate the alkene.

d) Yes. Thiol addition would require an acid catalyst because, though more acidic than an alcohol or water, it is not acidic enough to protonate the alkene.

8.31

The addition of a nucleophile to a three-membered ring usually proceeds with *anti*-stereochemistry in order for the filled orbitals of the nucleophile to overlap with the empty σ* orbital of the carbon-leaving group bond. In a three-membered ring, this means the nucleophile must approach from the face of the ring opposite the leaving group.

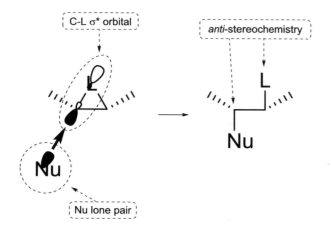

8.33

a) This is a formal addition of H_2O to an alkene. The alkene would be

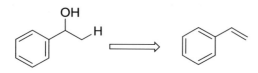

(racemic)

Either acid catalyzed addition of water (e.g. H_2SO_4(cat), H_2O) or oxymercuration in water ($Hg(OAc)_2$, H_2O) followed by a reductive removal of the mercury with $NaBH_4$.

b) This is addition of water to an alkene. In order to get the –OH group on the carbon atom indicated, that carbon must be the site of the most stable carbocation intermediate.

(racemic)

The reagents are similar to those of part (a): acid catalyzed addition of water (e.g., H_2SO_4(cat), H_2O) or oxymercuration in water ($Hg(OAc)_2$, H_2O) followed by a reductive removal of the mercury with $NaBH_4$. Note that the oxymercuration is the preferred route, as the acid catalyzed reaction may lead to a rearranged product.

c) The alkene must include the carbon to which the –OH has added, so the only possibility is

However, a Markovnikov addition to this would give the wrong product.

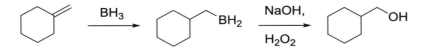

So, hydroboration followed by oxidation is needed (anti-Markovnikov addition).

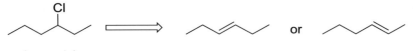

d) Formation of this product would involve HCl addition. However, there are two possible alkenes that could be considered.

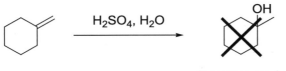

Considering the possible products of each:

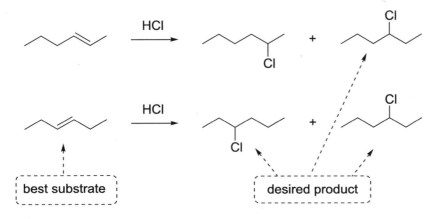

3-hexene leads only to the desired regioisomer, but 2-hexene produces two regioisomers. 3-hexene will be the better starting material.

e) There are two alkenes to consider. Using Cl_2 as reagent, the two chlorine atoms will add stereospecifically with a *trans* orientation.

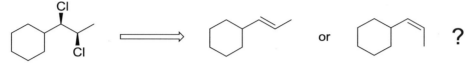

(racemic)

The *trans* alkene does not give the correct stereochemistry.

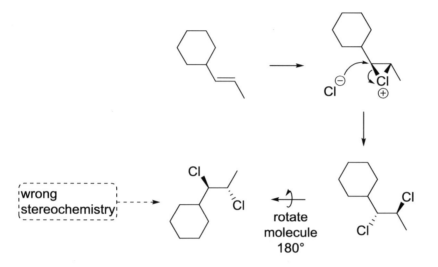

The *cis* alkene does lead to the correct final product.

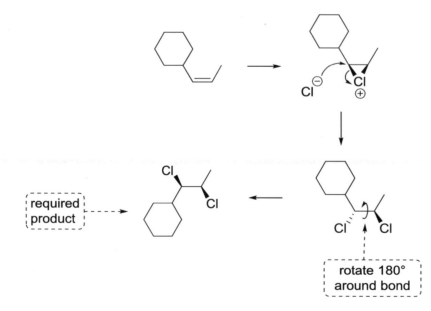

f) One way to get a mixture of diastereomers is to invert all but one of the chiral centres.

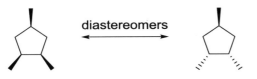

These two alkanes can be formed from the same alkene by addition of hydrogen across different faces of the double bond.

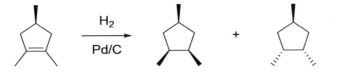

8.35

a) The first step is hydrogenation, with a poisoned catalyst giving only a single reduction.

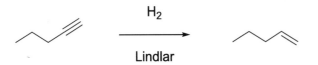

Then, the resulting alkene undergoes hydroboration.

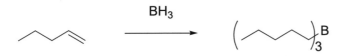

Oxidative removal of the borane gives the final alcohol product.

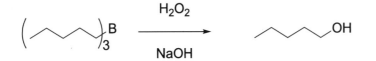

b) In the second sequence, a sterically hindered borane would first add to the alkyne.

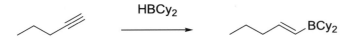

Then, oxidative removal of the borane group would lead to an intermediate enol, which would rearrange into an aldehyde.

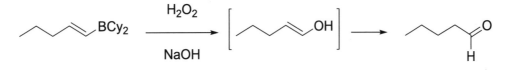

c) In the third sequence, the first step is hydration of one of the π bonds, forming an enol that rearranges into the more stable ketone.

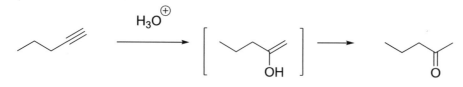

The second step uses borohydride to reduce the ketone to an alcohol.

8.37

a) This would be a simple Markovnikov addition of water to the double bond. So, either acid catalyzed hydration or oxymercuration followed by reductive workup with sodium borohydride will form the product.

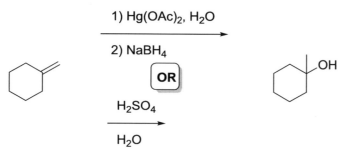

b) This is a Markovnikov addition of methanol to the alkene. Using methanol with an acid catalyst or oxymercuration in methanol followed by reduction would give the desired product.

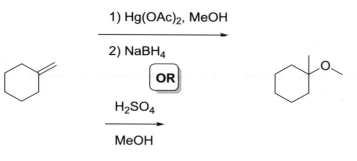

c) The formation of this halohydrin requires bromine in water, since the water would add to the initial bromonium ion to produce the regiochemistry required.

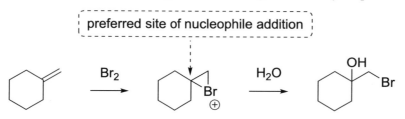

d) To form this halohydrin, the nucleophile used last will be the bromide. Formation of an epoxide with mCPBA followed by bromide ion under acidic conditions gives the desired regiochemistry.

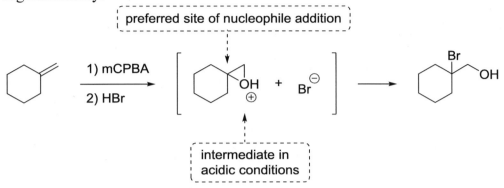

e) This is anti-Markovnikov addition of water. So, a borane is needed to add the initial hydrogen with this regiochemistry. The borane can be removed oxidatively to give the final alcohol.

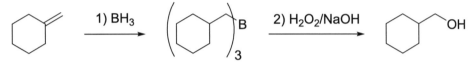

f) This is an epoxidation reaction with mCPBA.

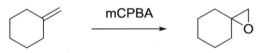

g) The product is obtained by addition of HCl to the double bond.

h) This is a catalytic addition of hydrogen over palladium on carbon.

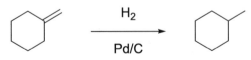

8.39

a) The first step in the reaction is analogous to addition of Br₂ to an alkene.

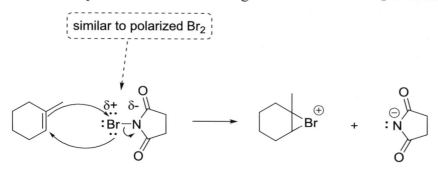

In the next step, the fluoride ion acts as a nucleophile to open the bromonium ion. The stereochemistry of the fluoride addition is controlled by two factors. First, F⁻ adds *trans* to the bromine atom. Second, F⁻ adds to the most-substituted carbon, which will have the most carbocation character.

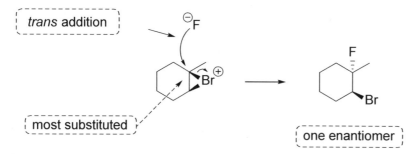

Since the initial bromonium ion is a racemic mixture of enantiomers, so must be the products, one of which is shown above.

b) The product shown in part (a) redrawn in chair conformation:

c) The product in part (b) flipped to the other chair conformation:

d) The configurations are assigned as shown below.

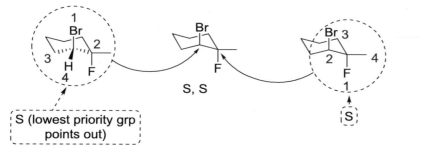

8.41

The bromine can add to a C–C double bond. The enol-keto equilibrium is the source of the C–C double bond. A bromonium ion is the product of the first step.

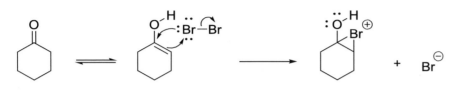

The nearby lone pairs on the –OH group can act as an internal nucleophile, opening up the bromonium ring. The protonated ketone is then deprotonated by the bromide ion acting as a base.

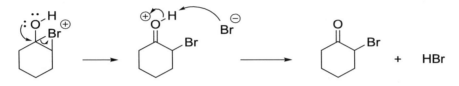

MCAT Style Problems

8.43

Answer: (a). The first step determines the reaction rate, since the addition of the bromine creates a bromonium intermediate of high energy.

8.45

Add the chlorine atoms *trans* to each other, then rotate into the conformation shown.

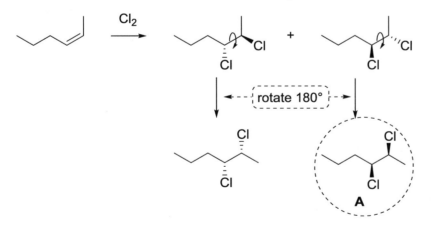

Challenge Problem

8.47

The –OH group is acting as a nucleophile. The first step is carbocation formation by adding a proton to the alkene. The –OH group then reacts at the tertiary carbocation, forming a bicyclic ring system. The chloride ion then deprotonates the intermediate to make the final product.

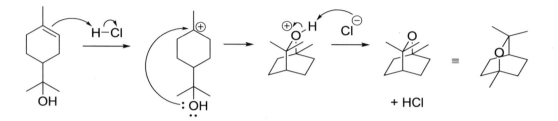

PROBLEMS

9.13

The number of π electrons and their types are shown below each molecule. (BP = π bond electron. LP = lone pair in a p orbital.)

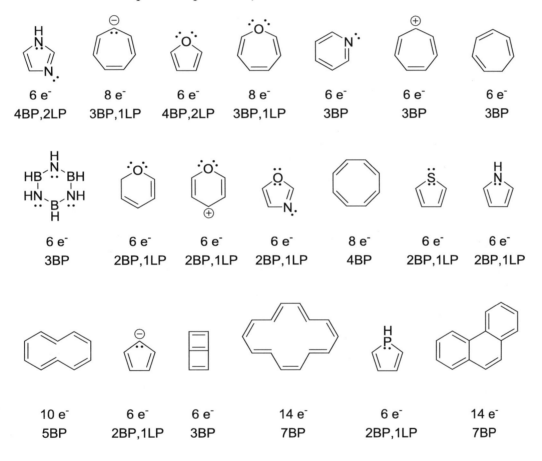

6 e⁻	8 e⁻	6 e⁻	8 e⁻	6 e⁻	6 e⁻	6 e⁻
4BP,2LP	3BP,1LP	4BP,2LP	3BP,1LP	3BP	3BP	3BP

6 e⁻	6 e⁻	6 e⁻	6 e⁻	8 e⁻	6 e⁻	6 e⁻
3BP	2BP,1LP	2BP,1LP	2BP,1LP	4BP	2BP,1LP	2BP,1LP

10 e⁻	6 e⁻	6 e⁻	14 e⁻	6 e⁻	14 e⁻
5BP	2BP,1LP	3BP	7BP	2BP,1LP	7BP

9.15

The compounds from Question 9.13 are grouped below. For the non-aromatics, the reason for this is given.

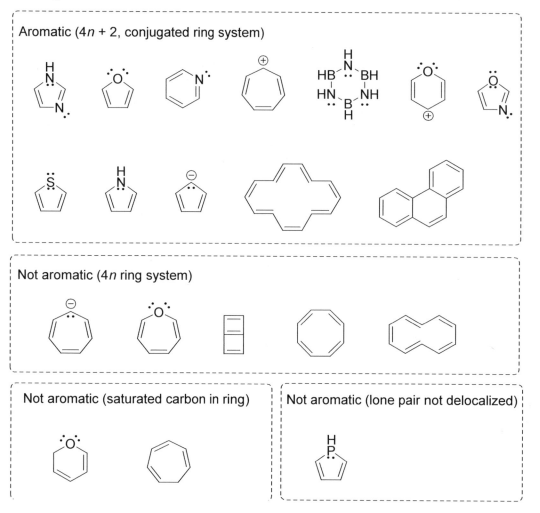

9.17

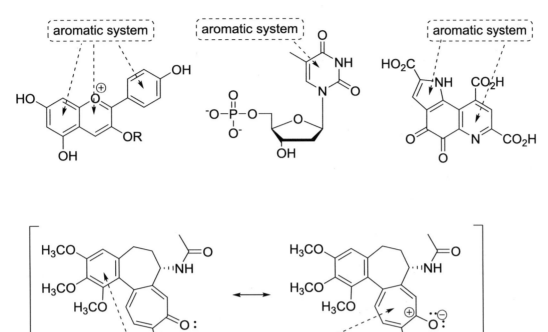

9.19

The difference in appearance between napthlene and azulene arises because of the different resonance forms for each molecule. Napthalene has no charged resonance forms, but azulene has many forms with charge separation (one of which is shown below).

naphthalene

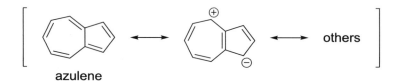

azulene   others

Both azulene rings are six-electron aromatic systems as charged species, so it has a dipole, as depicted below.

dipole moment   dipole moment

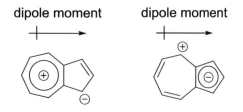

9.21

In order for the nitrogen to act as a base, it must use a lone pair to bond to the hydrogen atom. The lone pair should not be in an aromatic system since forming the N–H bond will break up the aromaticity.

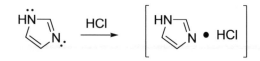

imidazole   imidazole hydrochloride

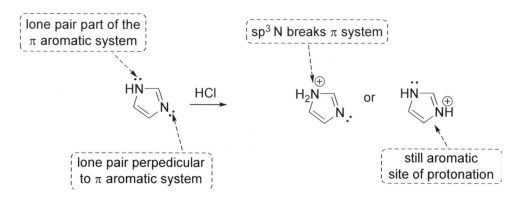

lone pair part of the π aromatic system

sp³ N breaks π system

lone pair perpedicular to π aromatic system

still aromatic site of protonation

9.23

The enol form, pyridine-2-ol, is favoured because it has an aromatic system in that tautomer. The keto form, pyridin-2-one, does not have an aromatic ring.

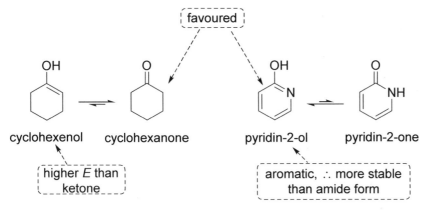

cyclohexenol   cyclohexanone   pyridin-2-ol   pyridin-2-one

higher *E* than ketone

aromatic, ∴ more stable than amide form

9.25

Cycloprop-2-enone would be more polar. The zwitterion resonance form for it has an aromatic ring. This would make that a large contributor to the overall resonance structure. The comparable form for cyclopropanone has no extra stabilizing factors and would be a very minor contributor.

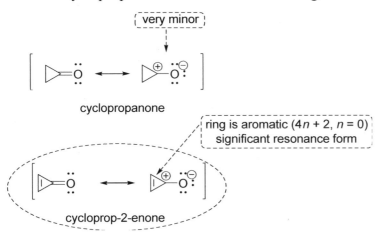

very minor

cyclopropanone

ring is aromatic ($4n + 2$, $n = 0$) significant resonance form

cycloprop-2-enone

The charge separation would increase the polarity, making cycloprop-2-enone the more polar molecule.

9.27

Adenine has an obvious six-membered aromatic ring. Resonance structures are given for the other three bases that show their aromatic character.

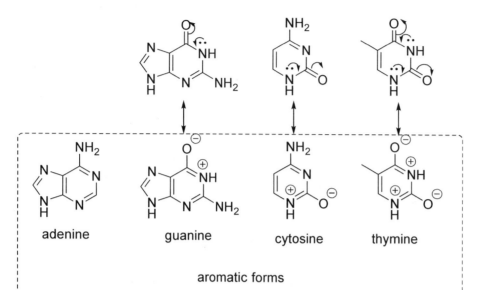

aromatic forms

9.29

The four compounds are numbered for easier discussion.

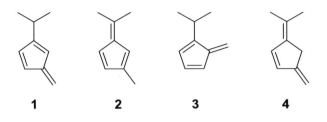

1   **2**   **3**   **4**

Removing the protons indicated below on **1**, **2**, and **4** produce the same anion and would have the same acidity.

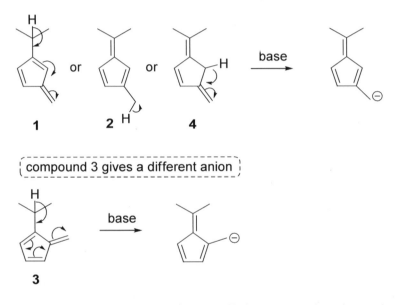

The anions from **1**, **2**, and **4** are all the same. They have three resonance forms, which delocalize the negative charge.

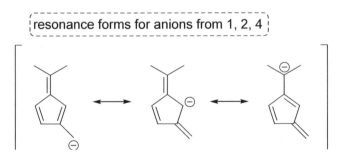

The anion from compound **3** has four resonance forms, which delocalize the negative charge.

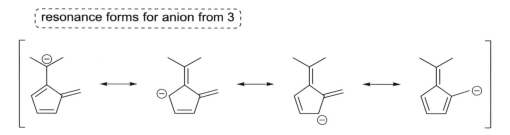

Compound **2** has an alternative allylic cation that can be abstracted, which gives rise to a cyclopentadienyl anion, an aromatic system. This is, therefore, the most acidic proton.

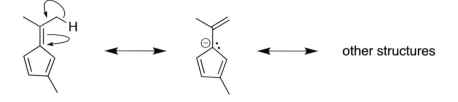

other structures

9.31

Deprotection step:

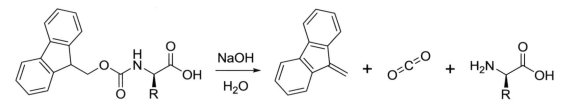

The enhanced acidity of the removed proton arises from aromatic stabilization of the anion formed. The mechanism for the removal is shown below.

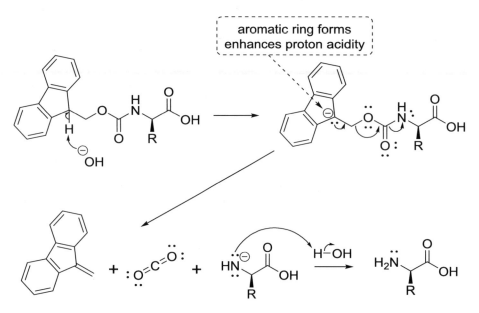

aromatic ring forms enhances proton acidity

MCAT Style Problems

9.33

Answer: (b). Its HOMOs are completely filled with electrons.

a)   Its HOMOs are half-filled with electrons. (This is the condition for anti-aromaticity.)

c)   Its LUMOs are half-filled with electrons. (LUMO is unoccupied by definition.)

d)   Its LUMOs are completely filled with electrons. (LUMO is unoccupied by definition.)

9.35

Answer: (a). Cyclooctatetraene is not planar, because it disrupts conjugation and avoids anti-aromaticity.

Challenge Problem

9.36

The reaction to be accounted for is redrawn below.

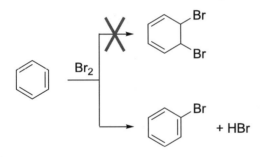

The reaction that does occur would appear to be

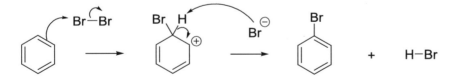

The driving force for this would be that removing the proton indicated restores aromaticity to the benzene ring. The addition process removes the aromaticity, making it a higher-energy process than it would be in a simple alkene.

So, the lower energy process is the substitution of a hydrogen with a bromine.

In practice, this reaction actually requires a Lewis acid catalyst such as $FeBr_3$, which can be added directly to the reaction or formed *in situ* by Fe in the presence of Br_2.

Chapter 10
Synthesis Using Aromatic Materials:
Electrophilic Aromatic Substitution and Directed Ortho Metalation

PROBLEMS

10.21

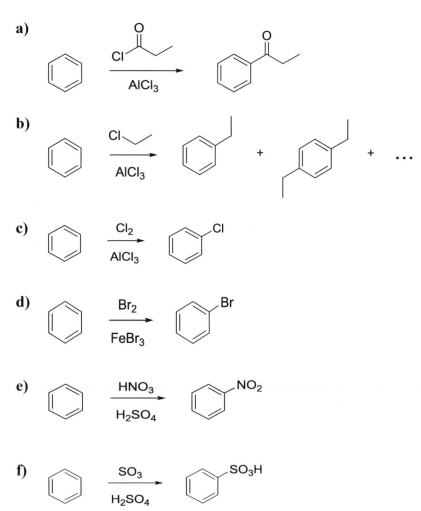

a)

b)

c)

d)

e)

f)

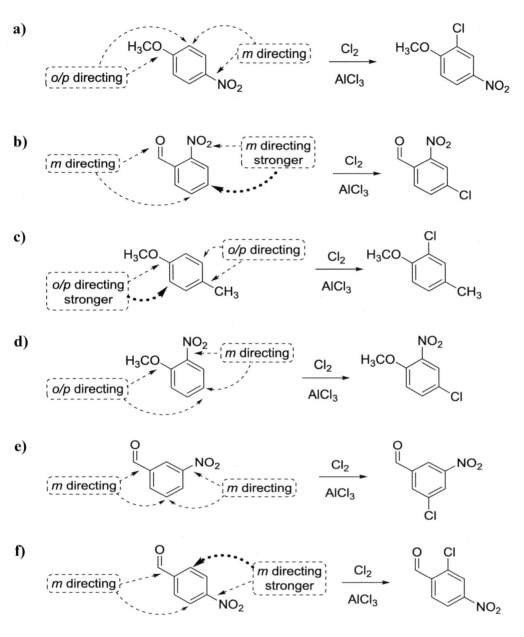

a)

b)

c)

d)

e)

f)

g) The groups are reinforcing each other's directing properties. The site *para* to the methoxy is less sterically hindered and probably the preferred site of substitution.

h) Both groups are strong activators/deactivators and in competition. Without a quantitative measure of their relative effects, either could direct the regiochemistry of the final product.

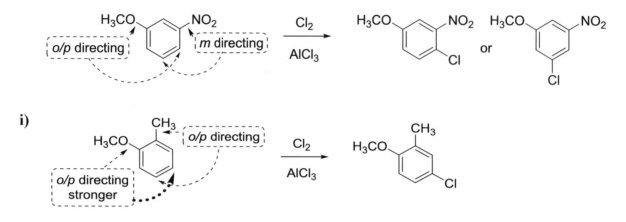

i)

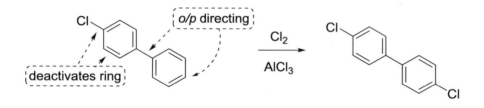

j) The chlorinated ring will be less reactive than the other ring.

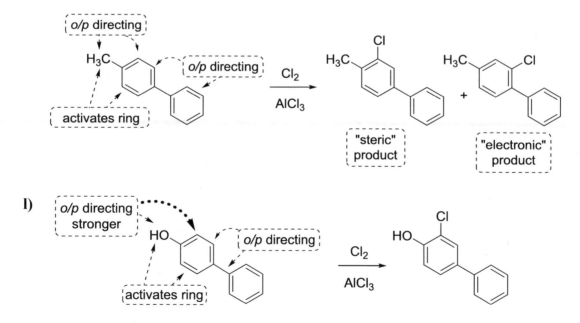

k) Both groups are weakly activating *o/p* directors and are in competition. The phenyl could be a stronger director based on resonance contribution to the arenium, giving the "electronic" product. If steric considerations are more important, the *ortho* site to the methyl group is less sterically hindered and could lead to the "steric" product.

l)

10.25

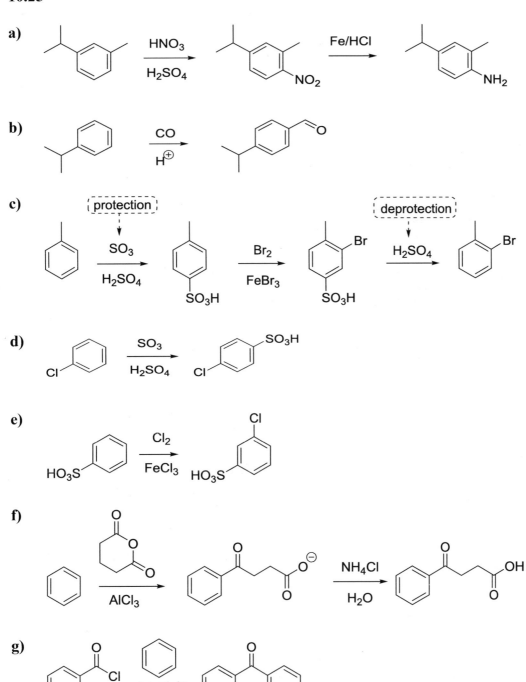

h)

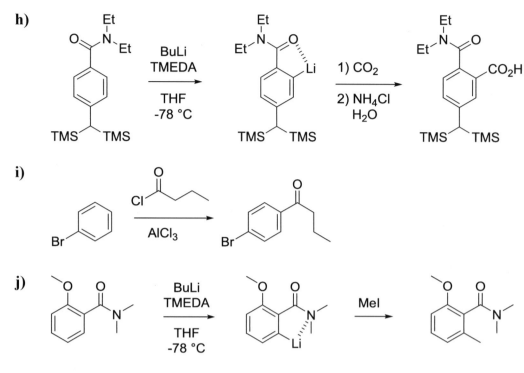

i)

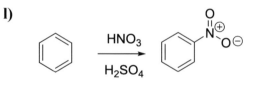

j)

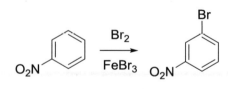

k)

l)

m)

n)

10.27

a) Direct alkylation would fail since the 1°carbocation would rearrange to a more stable 2°carbocation. Acylation followed by a reduction to the alkyl avoids this complication.

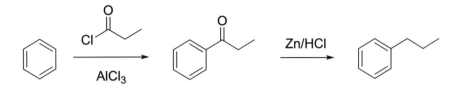

b) Two additions are required to make the final product. The order is important to get the substitution pattern required. Chlorine is *o/p* directing and NO$_2$ is *m* directing. Since the substitution is meta, the NO$_2$ group should be added first.

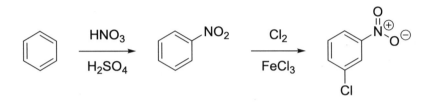

c) Two additions are required to make the final product. The order is important to get the substitution pattern required. Bromine is *o/p* directing and the acyl group is *meta* directing. Since the substitution is *meta*, the acyl group should be added first.

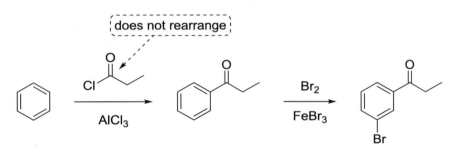

d) Two additions are required. The directing properties of the amide group can be used to ensure the proper substitution pattern. The bromine is first added to the *para* position due to the *o/p* directing of the amide group. In the second step, chlorine adds *ortho* to the amide since the amide is the stronger *o/p*-directing group.

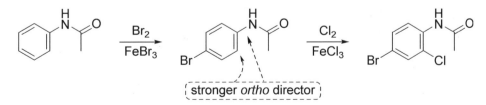

e) Two additions are required. The directing properties of the methoxy group can be used to ensure the proper substitution pattern. The ethyl group is first added to the *para* position due to the *o/p* directing of the methoxy group. In the second step, methyl adds *ortho* to the methoxy since methoxy is the stronger *o/p*-directing group.

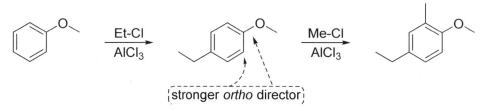

f) The nitro is *meta* directing, so the Cl should be added first. If the *o/p* directing of the chloro group is strong enough to outweigh the *meta* directing of the NO$_2$ group, it should promote bromination at the least hindered *o/p* site, which is *para* to the NO$_2$ group.

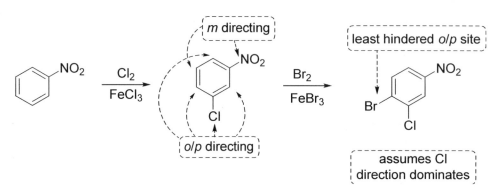

A better synthesis that does not require competition between directing groups would be to modify the nitro group by reduction to the *ortho/para*-directing amine. Bromination of aniline *para* to the amine followed by oxidation of the amine back to a nitro group, and subsequent chlorination, would give more certain results.

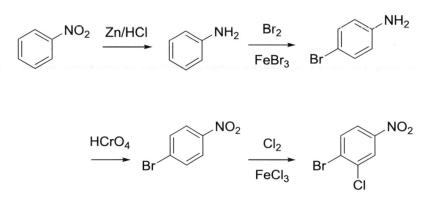

Copyright © 2018 Nelson Education Limited

10.29

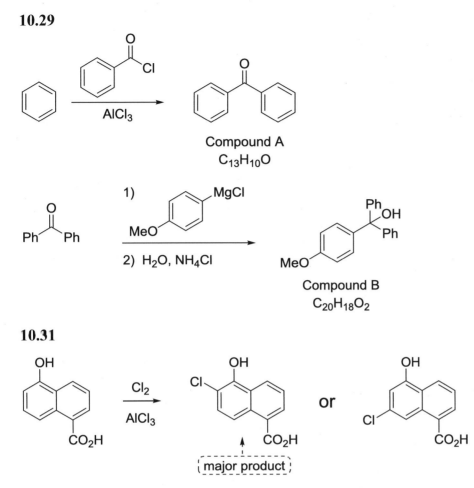

Compound A
C$_{13}$H$_{10}$O

Compound B
C$_{20}$H$_{18}$O$_2$

10.31

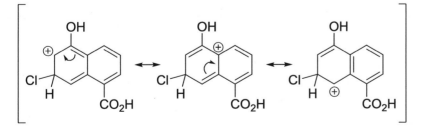

major product

In the intermediate for the major product, the OH group helps to delocalize the positive charge, stabilizing the arenium ion.

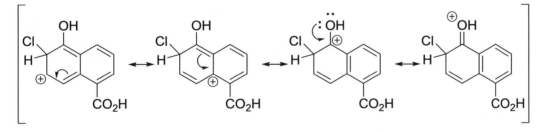

The other intermediate arenium ion has no extra stability contributed from the OH group.

The major product will be produced by formation of the most stable intermediate (lowest-energy pathway).

10.33

a) The product is a combination of two molecules of the starting alkene.

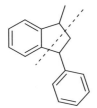

One alkene is protonated forming a carbocation. The carbocation is then attacked by the nucleophilic π bond on a second molecule of starting material. The resulting carbocation then reacts with the aromatic ring, and the final product is produced by deprotonation by the conjugate base of the acid used.

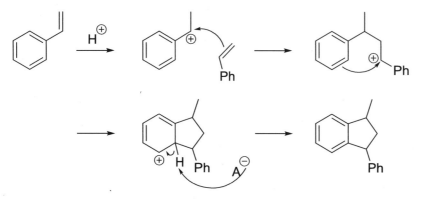

b) In order for the rings to couple, a carbocation has to form in one of the aromatic rings.

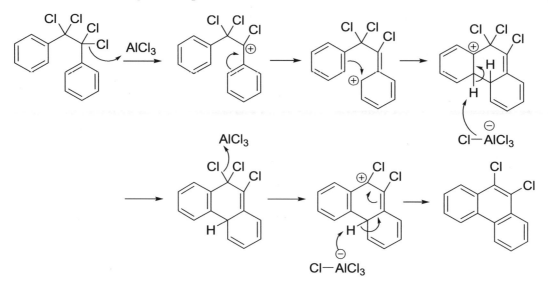

c) The overall reaction involves a loss of H_2O. Protonation of the alcohol creates a carbocation, which can rearrange to relieve some bond angle strain in the molecule and form a more stable secondary carbocation intermediate.

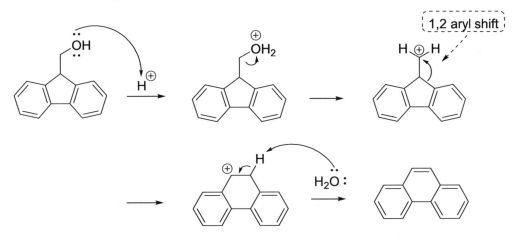

10.35

The nitrite will react with HCl to form nitrosyl chloride. The nitrogen is electrophilic and reacts with the aromatic ring electrons to form the final product.

NOCl formation

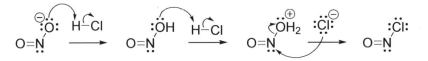

Nitration

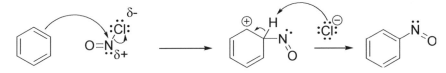

10.37

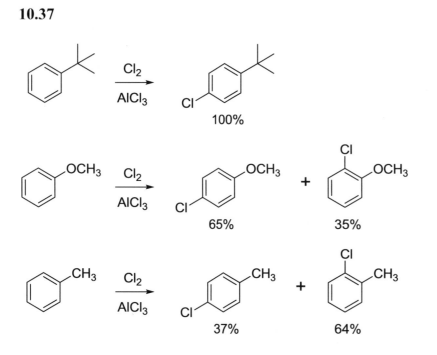

100%

65%   35%

37%   64%

The very large *t*-butyl group (A > 4) blocks reactivity at the *ortho* position completely, giving *para* substitution exclusively in the first reaction.

The methoxy group in anisole is a strong activating group, with electron donation to the *o/p* positions shown in the resonance forms below.

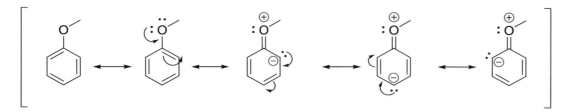

The preference for *para* substitution could be due to the methoxy group blocking *ortho* attack to some extent.

The methyl group in toluene is a weak *o/p* activator. The electron donation is from hyperconjugation and is distance dependent. It will have a greater influence on the *ortho* position than the *para* position as a result. This would account for the observed preference for *ortho* substitution in toluene.

10.39

Both groups are potential directors for metalation. In the bottom reaction, the amine is the preferred director because the less electronegative nitrogen atom is the better electron donor and will better stabilize the lithium ion. The addition of TMEDA will produce a complexed lithium reagent, with the bulky TMEDA attached to the lithium atom. This complex is larger and reacts preferentially at the less sterically hindered methoxy end of the ring.

10.41

The first step is sulfonation of the phenol. The phenol can survive the reaction conditions and the final product is deactivated enough to withstand nitration conditions.

Sulfonation

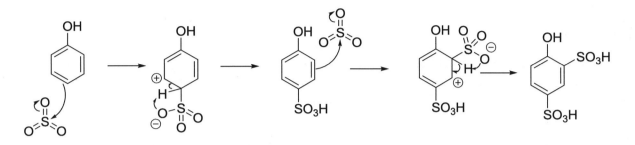

The first addition of a nitro group proceeds as usual.

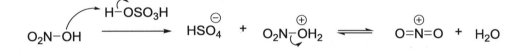

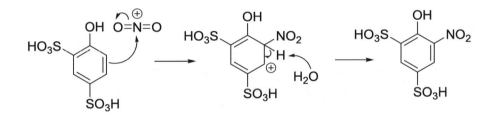

The final two nitrations occur at the sites of the sulfonate groups by a process known as *ipso*-nitration. In these additions, the leaving group is not a hydrogen but SO_3. The final two nitrations are shown below.

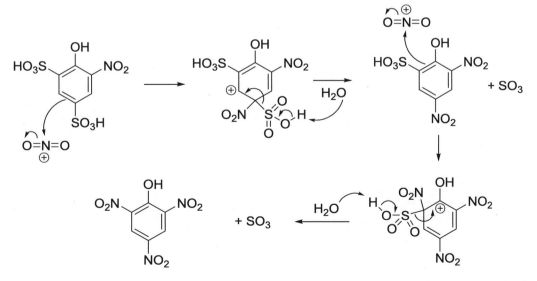

MCAT Style Problems

10.43

Answer: (a). Electron donation stabilizes cationic intermediates and increases reactivity.

Challenge Problems

10.45

The phenol is acidic and so will be deprotonated by the hydroxide.

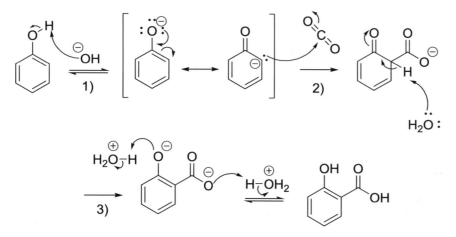

10.46

The ester group is similar to an acyl halide used in Fridel–Crafts reactions. Complexation by the Lewis acid would activate the group, making it susceptible to attack by the aromatic ring electrons.

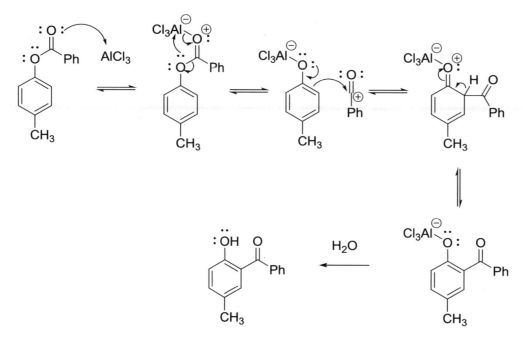

Chapter 11
Displacement Reactions
on Saturated Carbons:
S_N1 and S_N2 Substitution Reactions

PROBLEMS

11.17

a)

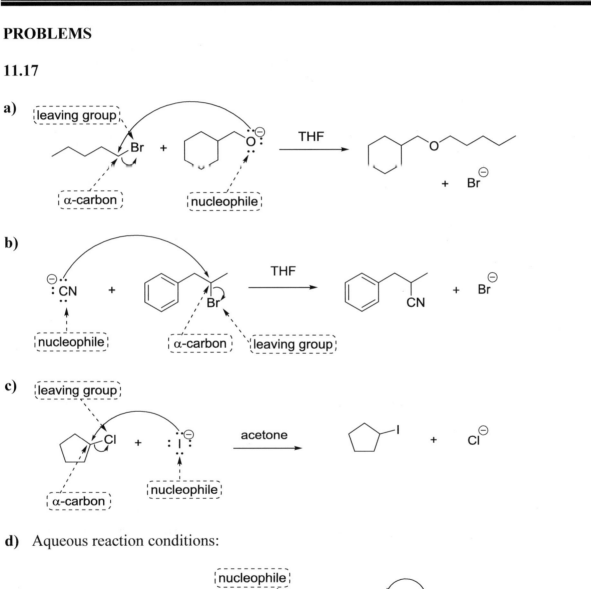

b)

c)

d) Aqueous reaction conditions:

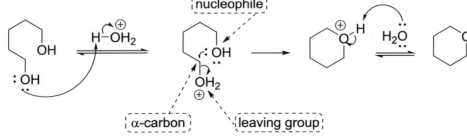

e)

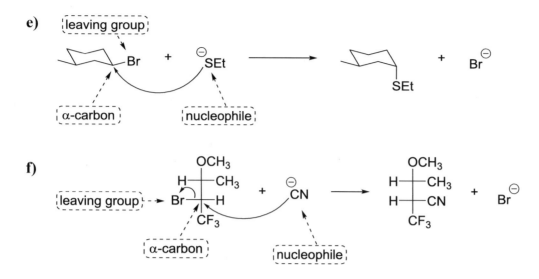

f)

11.19

The reaction rate would be increased. The base is very bulky and so would not be an effective nucleophile. It would deprotonate the thiol, making it a charged nucleophile. Charged nucleophiles are more effective in substitution reactions than neutral ones.

$(CH_3)_3CO^{\ominus}$ + $H{-}SCH_2CH_3$ $\longrightarrow$ $(CH_3)_3COH$ + $^{\ominus}SCH_2CH_3$

11.21

The most-reactive molecule in an S_N2 reaction is circled.

a) The amine would be the better nucleophile, giving the faster reaction.

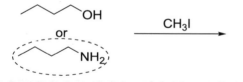

b) In both of the amines, there would be little steric hinderance to consider, as the reactive α-carbon only has hydrogen atoms attached. The secondary amine would be more nucleophilic due to electron donation from two alkyl groups, making the nitrogen more electron rich.

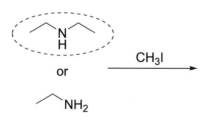

c) Bromide is a better leaving group than chloride.

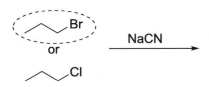

d) The α-carbon is less sterically hindered in the primary alkyl bromide and would react faster.

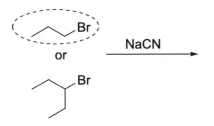

e) The alkoxide is a better nucleophile than the carboxylate. The charge in the carboxylate is delocalized through resonance, reducing both its nucleophilicity and basicity.

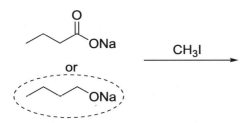

11.23

a)

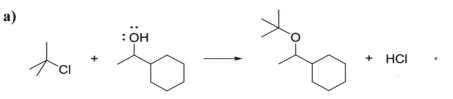

b) The alkyl halide is tertiary, so the reaction would proceed via an S$_N$1 mechanism.

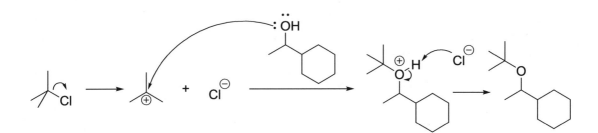

c) The rate is governed by the rate of formation of the carbocation. Increasing the alkyl halide concentration would increase the rate. The rate would also be increased by using a polar protic solvent to help stabilize the carbocation.

d) The reaction rate would be increased. The carbocation would be stabilized by resonance and, thus, form more easily.

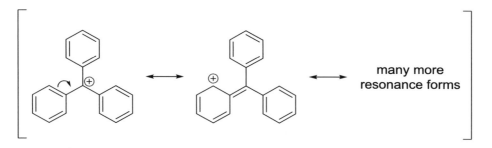

11.25

a) Disconnection on either side of sulfur atom gives the same pairs of sulfur nucleophile and two-carbon electrophile.

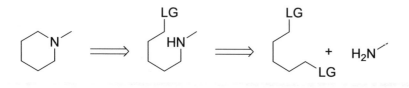

There is more than one choice for the electrophile. One example would be

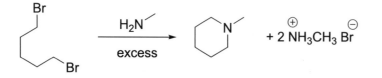

b) Two disconnection steps show that a bifunctional starting material is needed.

Again, there are many choices for the leaving group that could work. One example is

c)

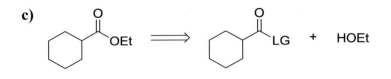

Standard ester disconnection leads to a variety of possible electrophiles. One example would be

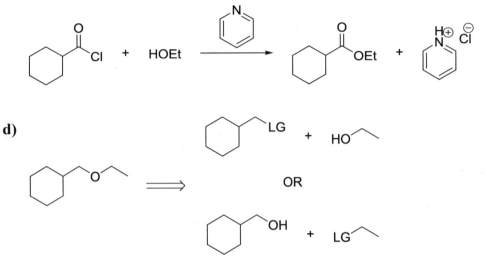

d)

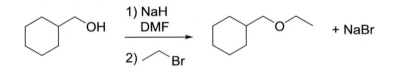

Like thioethers, ethers are disconnected on either side of the oxygen atom to give two possible synthetic approaches. One possible reaction scheme is given below.

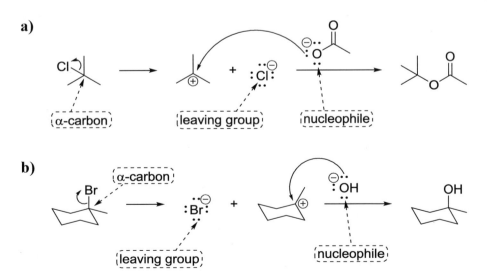

11.27

a)

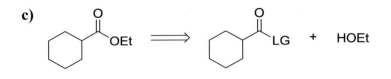

b)

c)

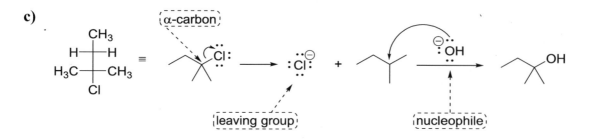

11.29

a) The reaction is enhanced by the presence of iodide ions. It is both a good nucleophile and a better leaving group than chloride. Having a better leaving group will increase the rate of the reaction.

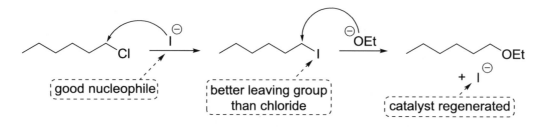

b) Iodide is the best leaving group amongst the halides and a good nucleophile. So, it can effectively substitute the chloride but will be displaced easily by the final nucleophilic substitution.

c) Tetraalkyl ammonium salts are very soluble in organic solvents. This makes the iodide ions accessible for reaction. Sodium salts are less soluble in organic solvents.

11.31

These are S$_N$1 reactions, so the product formed is determined by which available nucleophile reacts with the carbocation intermediate. In the first reaction, both water and cyanide ion are available. The product alcohol is the result of the water reacting more often than the cyanide. This is due to the large excess of water that would be present, making it much more probable for water to trap the carbocation.

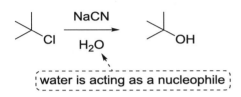

water is acting as a nucleophile

In the second reaction, there is no solvent addition due to the steric bulk of the alcohol. So, the cyanide would be the more effective nucleophile and lead to the nitrile product.

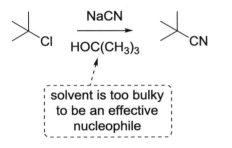

solvent is too bulky
to be an effective
nucleophile

11.33

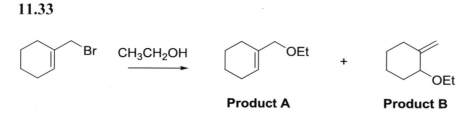

Product A **Product B**

Product A is easily accounted for by S$_N$2 substitution of the bromide by the alcohol nucleophile. **Product B** could be formed through an allylic carbocation intermediate (S$_N$1), which is stabilized by resonance.

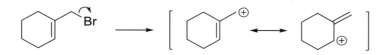

The ring has electrophilic carbon atoms (containing positive charges in the resonance forms) and both will be attacked by the nucleophilic alcohol, leading to a mixture of **Products A** and **B**. Note: There is another reaction mechanism not covered in the text, called *S$_N$2'*, that occurs with allylic alkyl halides, which could also account for **Product B**.

<u>S$_N$2' substitution</u>

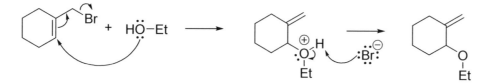

In practice, the products will be produced through a combination of the S$_N$1, S$_N$2, and S$_N$2' mechanistic pathways.

11.35

Since the carbon backbone is different in the product, there must be a carbocation intermediate that rearranges.

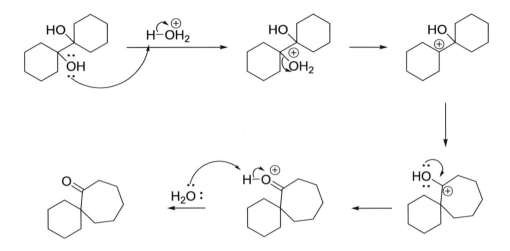

MCAT Style Problems

11.37

Answer: (c).

Step 1 makes an alkoxide, which is a nucleophile. The best leaving group in the second reagent is the chloride. Step 2 is probably an S_N1 substitution through an oxonium intermediate.

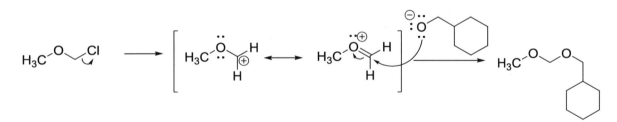

11.38

The product shown has retained the stereochemistry at the substituted carbon. Therefore, two S_N2 reactions must have occurred at the amine nitrogen, inverting the stereochemistry each time, leaving the product with the original configuration.

The three transformations that occur are:

- conversion of the amine to diazonium, making it a good leaving group
- S_N2 displacement of N_2 by the carboxylic acid hydroxyl group (first inversion)
- S_N2 displacement of the hydroxyl group by water to form the alcohol (second inversion)

The mechanism for the reaction is shown below.

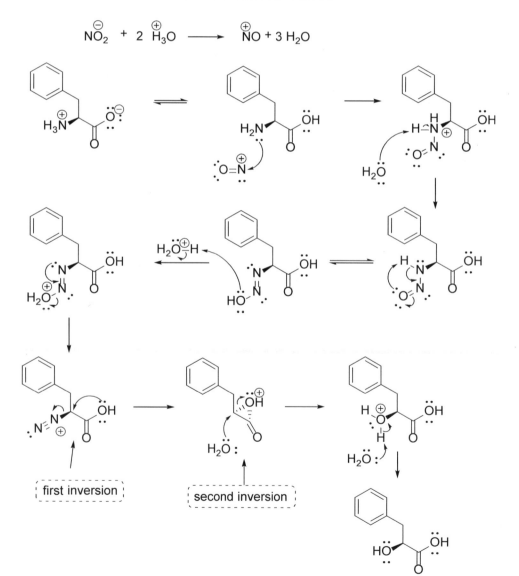

Chapter 12
The Formation of π Bonds
by Elimination Processes:
Elimination and Oxidation Reactions

PROBLEMS

12.15

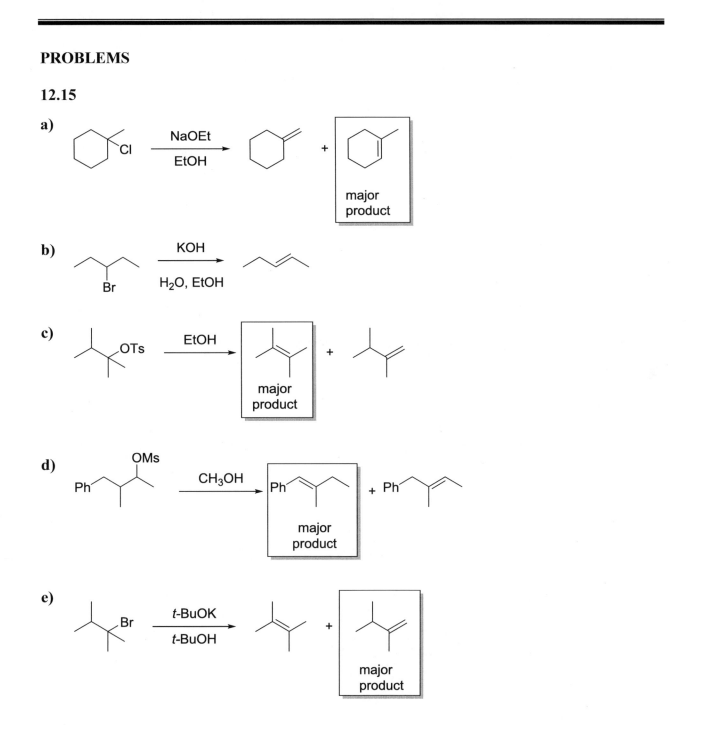

f)

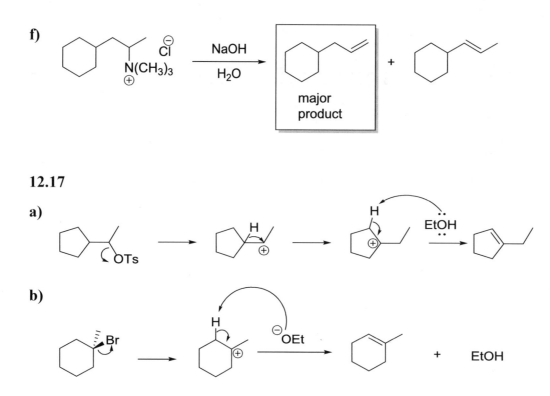

NaOH

H₂O

major
product

+

12.17

a)

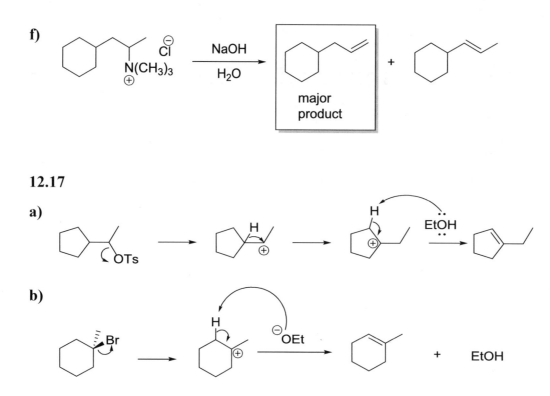

b)

EtOH

+   EtOH

12.19

There are two protons adjacent to the bromine that can be removed. In order to get the Hoffman product, H_b needs to be removed preferentially.

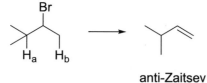

anti-Zaitsev
product

This can be accomplished by using a sterically hindered base so that it cannot easily get close to H_a and remove it.

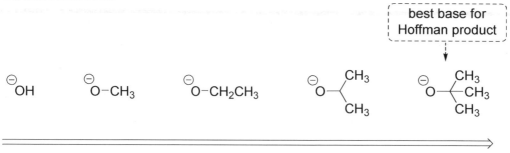

⊖OH   ⊖O–CH₃   ⊖O–CH₂CH₃

best base for
Hoffman product

increasing steric bulk,
increasing Hoffman product

12.21

a) Concentrated acid and heat favour dehydration.

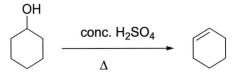

b) An oxidizing agent is required.

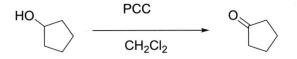

c) A strong oxidizing reagent for alcohols would work here.

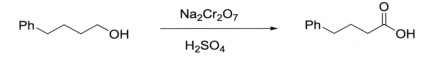

d) A bulky base is needed to produce the Hofmann product.

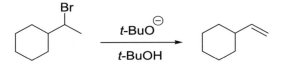

e) The tosylate is a good leaving group.

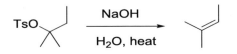

12.23

a)

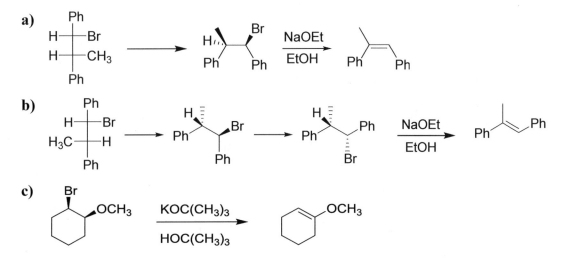

b)

c)

d)

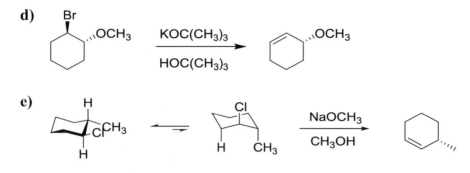

e)

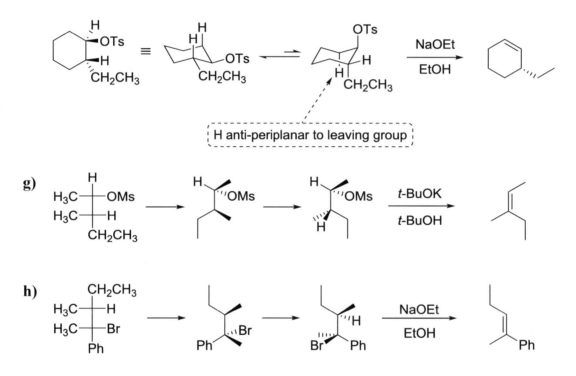

f) Only one adjacent hydrogen can attain an anti-periplanar orientation to the tosyl leaving group.

g)

h)

12.25

This is a tertiary alkyl halide and should react through a carbocation intermediate. H_a and H_b are the two possible sites for deprotonation in the carbocation. H_a is more acidic and should be more reactive. Removing H_a also leads to a resonance-stabilized product.

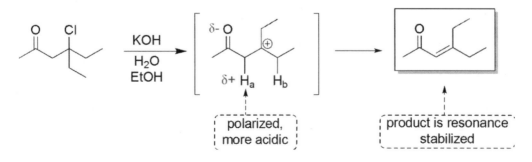

12.27

The two steps in the degradation are shown below.

Step 1

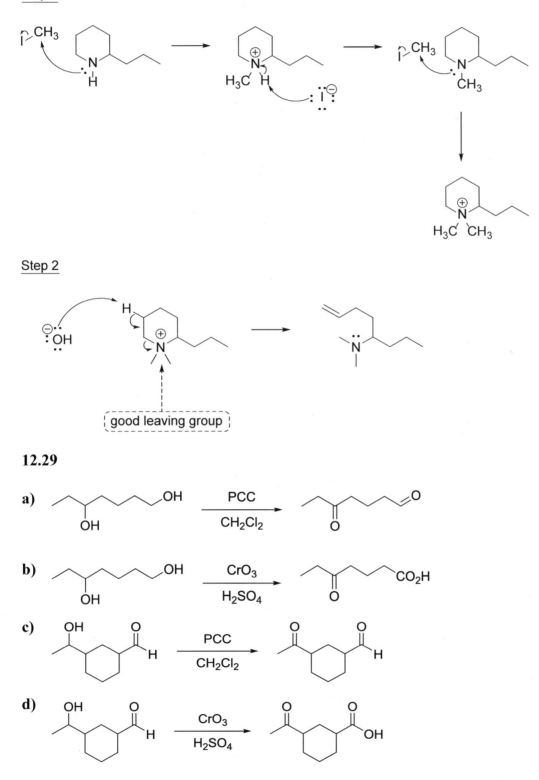

Step 2

12.29

a)

b)

c)

d)

12.31

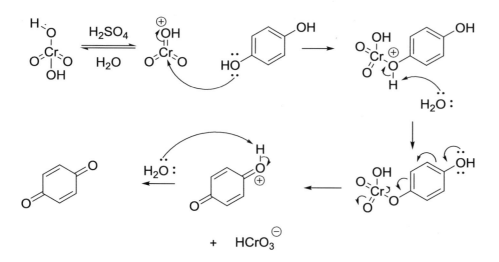

$$+ \quad HCrO_3^{\ominus}$$

MCAT Style Problems

12.33

Answer: (b). There is a net loss of two hydrogens, forming a ketone from an alcohol.

Challenge Problem

12.34

a) The starting material:

Mass: 213.11
C, 56.36%; H, 6.15%; Br, 37.49%

(R)-(1-bromo-1-methylpropyl)benzene

b) The desired product:

Mass: 132.09
C, 90.85%; H, 9.15%

(Z)-(1-methyl-1-propenyl)benzene

c) An alcohol can form by nucleophilic substitution with water.

d) Starting material:

Mass: 213.11
C, 56.36%; H, 6.15%

(1-bromo-1-methylpropyl)benzene

e) A longer reaction time or heat would cause more of the starting material to be consumed.

f) Minor product 2 is the alkene.

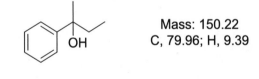

Mass: 132.09
C, 90.85; H, 9.15

g)

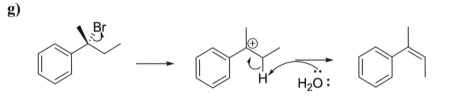

h) The major product is the alcohol.

Mass: 150.22
C, 79.96; H, 9.39

i)

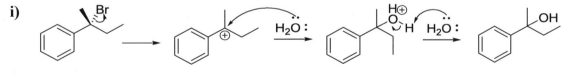

j) Heating the reaction would promote an E1 mechanism over an S_N1 reaction mechanism. This would lead to more of the desired product.

Chapter 13
Structure Determination I:
Nuclear Magnetic Resonance Spectroscopy

PROBLEMS

13.21

Highest and lowest electron density for hydrogens on sp³ carbons are shown.

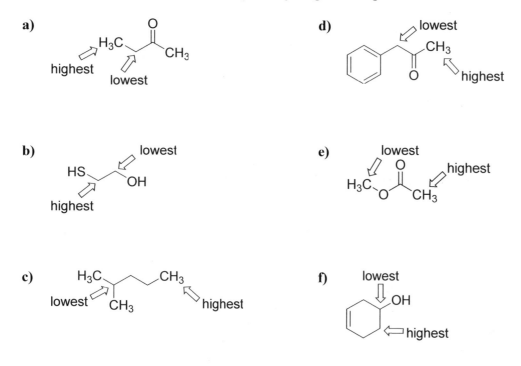

13.23

Because it is electrons that cause shielding, lowering the electron density is deshielding. This shifts the NMR signals downfield or to the left. The hydrogens with the highest electron density appear upfield or to the right.

13.25

a) The CH group is coupled to six methyl protons and the CH$_2$ group. It will appear as a very complicated multiplet.

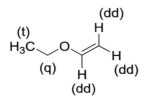

(multiplet)
looks like (pent)

b) The alkene protons are all inequivalent and coupled to each other.

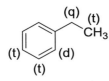

c) This structure has symmetry, so there are three types of aromatic protons.

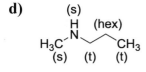

d)

```
        (s)
         H   (hex)
         N
  H₃C         CH₃
   (s)  (t)   (t)
```

e)

```
   (s)     (t) (pent)   (t)
  H₃C                  CH₃
         CH₃  (dt) (hex)
```

f)

```
   (t)    O
  H₃C        H
    (dq)   (t)
```

13.27

Groups corresponding to the signals shown are indicated in boldface in the fragments.

a) The integration near 6 suggests two equivalent methyl groups. Because it is a doublet, each methyl group is adjacent to one hydrogen, which must be between them so that the methyl groups are equivalent.

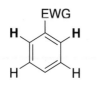

b) A two-hydrogen triplet is a CH_2 next to two hydrogens. The chemical shift suggests that it is also adjacent to an electron-withdrawing group like a carbonyl, iodide, amine, or aromatic ring.

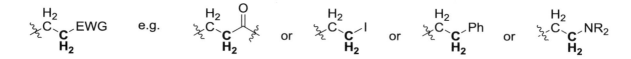

c) This signal has the same integration and coupling as (a), though it is slightly farther downfield, suggesting that there is an electron-withdrawing group nearby.

H₃C
HC—EWG
H₃C

d) Two hydrogens in the aromatic region of a ^{1}H-NMR cannot indicate a CH_2, since each carbon can only be bonded to one hydrogen. The two equivalent hydrogens must be the same by symmetry. Each has one adjacent hydrogen, causing them to split into a doublet. The chemical shift upfield of 7.2 ppm indicates the presence of a strongly electron-withdrawing group on the ring.

EWG
H **H**
H H

e) The integration shows this is a single proton. The multiplet is symmetrical, which means that this is a first-order multiplet that can be analyzed in spite of its complexity. Looking at the peak heights, there are pairs that are 1:1 in height and some that are 1:3. This is a doublet of quartets, which suggests that the hydrogen we are observing is between a CH and a CH_3. The signal would appear as a pentet if both hydrogen types were freely rotating alkyl hydrogens with similar coupling constants. Instead, the CH_3 and CH couple differently, which means that one of them is likely on an alkene or aldehyde carbon. The signal we are looking at is next to a strongly electron-withdrawing group, based on the chemical shift. All this together gives us one of the two possible structures shown.

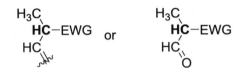

f) A three-hydrogen singlet is a methyl group with no adjacent hydrogen atoms. There is a strong electron-withdrawing functional group moving the signal downfield. This is

H_3C-EWG e.g. H_3C-O or H_3C-O

g) A two-hydrogen triplet is a CH_2 next to two hydrogens on another CH_2. The chemical shift past 3 ppm indicates that it is next to a strongly electron-withdrawing group like an oxygen or a chlorine.

h) This signal is a complicated multiplet and the integration of 1 indicates that it is a CH. A shift of 2.1 suggests that there is an electron-withdrawing functional group nearby, but not immediately adjacent; otherwise, the shift would have to be higher. In order for there to be enough adjacent protons for the observed splitting, this should be attached to a CH_2 group with an electron-withdrawing group on it to account for the chemical shift. A likely structure fragment would be

i) The chemical shift of these signals indicates the hydrogens are bonded to alkene carbons. The integration, 2:1, means that there are three total hydrogens. The lack of symmetry in the multiplet pattern suggests that two of the hydrogens are diastereotopic.

j) The chemical shift suggests that this hydrogen could be on a carbon adjacent to an alkene. The observed splitting would be due to the alkene proton.

k) This pattern is a heptet, which means that there are at least six adjacent hydrogens. The integration of 1 indicates that it is a CH. This is another isopropyl-type signal, similar to (h). A shift of 5.2 often indicates an alkene hydrogen; however, a CH bonded to two equivalent methyl groups cannot also have a double bond. In this case, the significant downfield shift suggests that there is a strongly electron-withdrawing functional group nearby, such as an ester or aryl ether.

$$H_3C\underset{CH_3}{\overset{H}{C}}EWG \quad e.g. \quad H_3C\underset{CH_3}{\overset{H}{C}}O\overset{O}{C} \quad or \quad H_3C\underset{CH_3}{\overset{H}{C}}O\text{-Ph}$$

l) A three hydrogen singlet is a methyl group immediately adjacent to a weaker electron-withdrawing functional group. For example, the chemical shift could be due to an iodide, a carbonyl, or an aromatic ring.

$$H_3C\text{-EWG} \quad e.g. \quad H_3C\overset{O}{C} \quad or \quad H_3C\text{-}\bigcirc \quad or \quad H_3C\text{-I}$$

m) Two hydrogens in the aromatic region of a ^{1}H-NMR cannot indicate a CH_2 since each carbon can only be bonded to one hydrogen. The two equivalent hydrogens must be the same by symmetry. Each has one adjacent hydrogen, causing them to split into a doublet. The chemical shift upfield of 7.2 ppm indicates the presence of an electron-withdrawing group on the ring.

n) The chemical shift indicates this is near an electron-withdrawing group like a ketone or an alkene. The integration would suggest this a CH_2 group and the splitting would be due to coupling to two other protons. The signal could be a triplet due to an adjacent CH_2 group or a doublet of doublets from two CH groups if the coupling constants are similar.

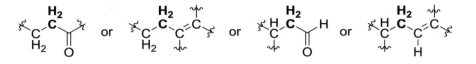

13.29

The actual chemical shifts are given; estimated answers should be reasonably close to these values.

a)

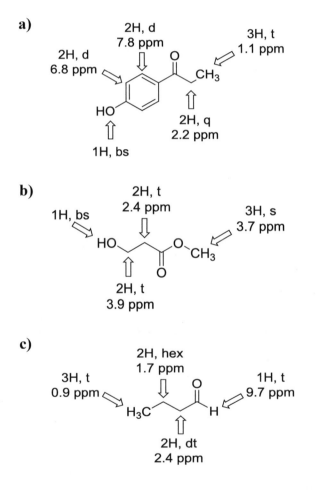

d)

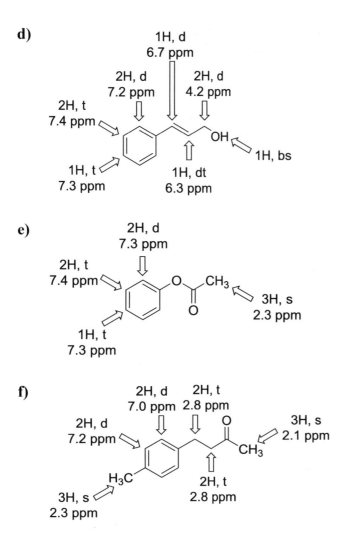

2H, t
7.4 ppm

2H, d
7.2 ppm

1H, d
6.7 ppm

2H, d
4.2 ppm

1H, bs

1H, t
7.3 ppm

1H, dt
6.3 ppm

e)

2H, d
7.3 ppm

2H, t
7.4 ppm

3H, s
2.3 ppm

1H, t
7.3 ppm

f)

2H, d
7.0 ppm

2H, t
2.8 ppm

2H, d
7.2 ppm

3H, s
2.1 ppm

3H, s
2.3 ppm

2H, t
2.8 ppm

13.31

a) The triplet and quartet are an ethyl group and the singlet is an isolated methyl group. Based on the chemical shift, there could be an alkene, aromatic ring, or carbonyl between the ethyl and methyl, but the absence of alkene or aromatic hydrogens makes the most likely structure a ketone. This is 2-butanone.

b) The coupling patterns in (b) are identical to those in (a); however, the chemical shift indicates that the CH_2 of the ethyl group is adjacent to the oxygen of an ester instead of a ketone. This is ethyl acetate.

c) The coupling patterns in (c) are identical to those in (a) and (b); however, the chemical shift indicates that it is the methyl group that is adjacent to the oxygen of an ester instead of the ethyl group. This is methyl propanate.

d) The singlet in (d) is similar to the singlets in (a) and (b), suggesting another methyl group next to a carbonyl. The downfield shift of what appears to be a pentet suggests another ester. There is a doublet that integrates for six hydrogens, which suggests that the pentet is actually a heptet that is difficult to see without magnification. This is isopropyl acetate.

e) An ethyl group that appears to be next to a carbonyl, based on the chemical shift and the absence of either aromatic or alkene signals, gives an incomplete molecule. In this case, the 2:3 integration ratio should be doubled to 2:6 so that you can complete 3-pentanone, a symmetrical ketone.

f) The pair of doublets around 7 ppm is a clear indication of a *para*-substituted aromatic ring. The signals are both upfield of 7.26 ppm, which is a sign that the ring has electron-donating groups. The other two signals are both isolated methyl groups. Based on the chemical shift, the one near 3.5 ppm is bonded to oxygen while the other is bonded to a carbonyl, an aromatic ring, or an alkene. There is no alkene, and a carbonyl would be electron-withdrawing to the ring. The structure is *p*-methylanisole.

g) There is a broad singlet at 13 ppm, indicating a carboxylic acid. The aromatic region has four distinct signals, both downfield and upfield of 7.26 ppm. From this, it appears that the ring has two substituents and no symmetry. The substituents must include both one electron-donating group and one electron-withdrawing group. The carboxylic acid is the electron-withdrawing group. The other signal is a methyl group that could be next to either an aromatic ring or a carbonyl. A methyl group bonded directly to an aromatic ring is slightly electron-donating, which matches the chemical shift of the aromatic signals. Alternately, the aromatic ring could be on the oxygen side of an ester. So far, the structure could be either of the following two, without specifying where the electron-donating group is relative to the acid.

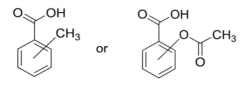

Para-substitution is not an option because it is symmetrical and would have two doublets in the aromatic region. Either *meta*- or *ortho*-substitution would allow there to be four different signals, though the coupling patterns would be different in each. Both substitution patterns would have two doublets; *ortho*-substitution would also have two triplets, which is what we observe. *Meta*-substitution would be expected to have only one triplet and a singlet.

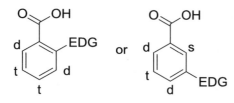

In either case, the different signals could overlap, which often makes distinguishing substitution difficult. This happens to be a very clear example of *ortho*-substitution. Based on the information given, the structure could be *either* of the two shown below. A ^{13}C-NMR would clearly identify the structure as acetylsalicylic acid, the structure on the right.

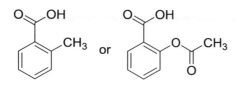

h) This spectrum closely resembles the one shown in part (f). The pair of doublets around 7 ppm is a clear indication of a *para*-substituted aromatic ring. The signals are both upfield of 7.26 ppm, which is a sign that the ring has electron-donating groups. The other two signals are both isolated methyl groups. Based on the chemical shift, both methyl groups can be bonded to a carbonyl, an aromatic ring, or an alkene. There is no alkene, and a carbonyl would be electron-withdrawing to the ring. It is tempting to put both methyl groups directly on the ring; however, doing that makes them equivalent, which they are not. The way to distinguish them while maintaining the electron-donating nature of the ring substitution is to make one of them an acetyl ester. The structure is *p*-tolylacetate.

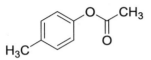

i) A two-hydrogen quartet and a three-hydrogen triplet is an ethyl group. The chemical shift indicates that the CH_2 is bonded to oxygen or chlorine. The structure so far is either chloroethane or CH_3-CH_2-O-. If the latter is the case, there is no end piece and the structure must be the symmetrical diethyl ether. The next chapter will deal with ways to distinguish these two possibilities.

$$H_3C\diagdown\diagup Cl \quad \text{or} \quad H_3C\diagdown\diagup O\diagdown\diagup CH_3$$

j) An aromatic region with five hydrogens indicates a monosubstituted ring. In this case, the close grouping around 7.26 ppm indicates an alkyl group, which is only weakly electron-donating. The one-hydrogen signal near 2.6 ppm is farthest downfield of the alkyl hydrogens, indicating that it is attached directly to the aromatic ring. Expansion shows that it is a hextet, adjacent to five hydrogens. This gives a $CH_3-CH-CH_2-$ fragment. The methyl group shows up as the doublet at 1.3 ppm. The CH_2 must be the pentet at 1.6 ppm, which is the only signal that integrates for two hydrogens. As a pentet, it must be adjacent to the CH and three additional hydrogens. Those three hydrogens are represented by the triplet at 0.9 ppm. The alkyl chain $CH_3-CH-CH_2-CH_3$, attached to the ring gives *sec*-butylbenzene. Notice that this structure has the potential to show second-order coupling because there is a stereocentre; however, all of the multiplets appear to be first order.

13.33

Both structures have four hydrogen types, suggesting a butyl bromide. The signal farthest downfield will be the hydrogen adjacent to the bromine.

a) In spectrum (a), the farthest downfield signal integrates as one hydrogen and is adjacent to five hydrogens. This must be 2-bromobutane.

b) In spectrum (b), the farthest downfield signal integrates as two hydrogens and is adjacent to a CH_2. This must be 1-bromobutane.

13.35

^{1}H-NMR:

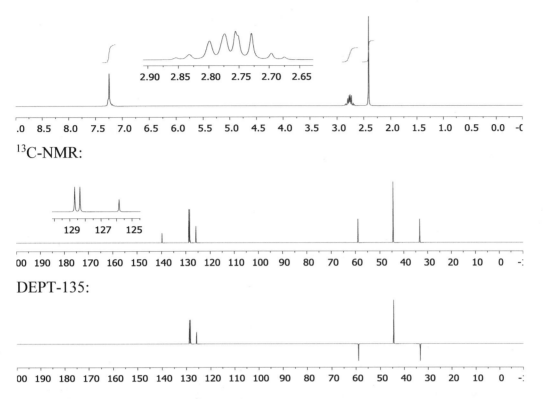

^{13}C-NMR:

DEPT-135:

There are three signals in the ^{1}H-NMR, with integrations of 5, 4, and 6. Based on the integration and chemical shift, the first signal represents a monosubstituted aromatic ring with a substituent that is neither strongly electron-withdrawing nor donating. The ^{13}C-NMR and DEPT-135 spectra support this, with four aromatic carbons and the signal at 140 ppm representing the substituted carbon.

The second ^{1}H-NMR signal, representing four hydrogens, is an overlap of two non-equivalent hydrogen types. The ^{13}C-NMR and DEPT-135 show the presence of two CH_2 carbons. Because the signals overlap, no information can be determined by the coupling.

The third ^{1}H-NMR signal is from two equivalent methyl groups, based on the integration and on the remaining ^{13}C-NMR/DEPT signal. The chemical shift of the methyl signal suggests that it is adjacent to an aromatic ring: a carbonyl or a nitrogen. Nitrogen is the only option that allows two methyl groups to be equivalent.

The fragments from the NMR spectra are the following:

Since the phenyl and the dimethylamino groups are both terminal, they must be separated by the two CH_2 groups.

13.37

¹H-NMR:

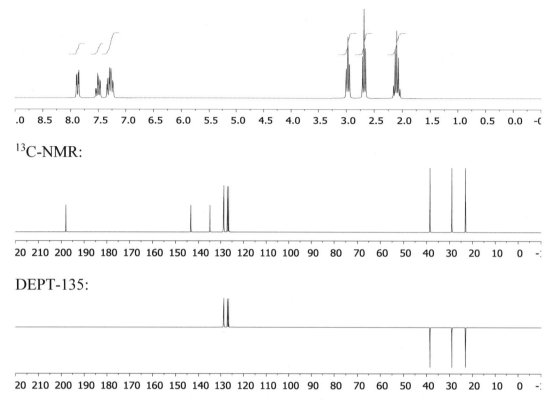

¹³C-NMR:

DEPT-135:

There are three aromatic hydrogen signals in the ¹H-NMR, representing four hydrogens. There are also three other CH₂ signals, based on the integration and the DEPT spectrum. The remaining signal in the ¹³C-NMR is a ketone, based on its chemical shift and lack of hydrogens.

The aromatic ring is di-substituted, based on the number of hydrogens. None of the fragments — a di-substituted aromatic ring, CH₂ groups, or a ketone — is a terminal group. This indicates that the substituents on the aromatic ring must form a ring. The two possibilities for a ring are the following:

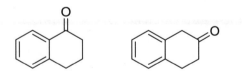

All of the CH2 groups are split by adjacent hydrogens. That, along with the downfield shift of the aromatic ring, indicates that the ketone is directly attached to the ring, and that the –CH₂–CH₂–CH₂– are contiguous. The correct structure is:

13.39

¹H-NMR:

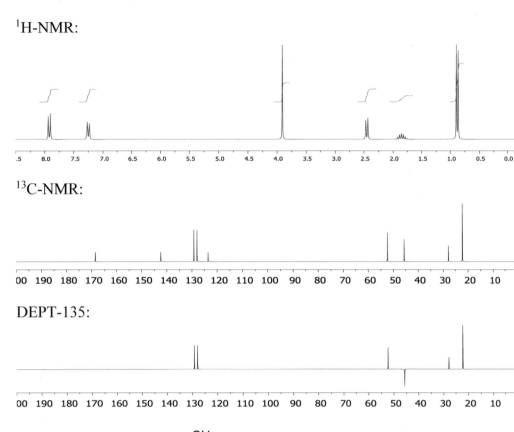

¹³C-NMR:

DEPT-135:

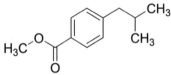

MCAT Style Problems

13.41

Answer: (a). The CH_2 adjacent to the ester O will be between 4 and 5 ppm.

The aromatic ring signals in (b) will be downfield of 6.5 ppm. The ketone signals in (c) will all be upfield of 3 ppm. The alcohol signals in (d) are all upfield of 4 ppm.

13.43

Answer: (b). Valine has an isopropyl side chain. Excluding the OH and NH_2 signals, that gives it three signals: two distinct CHs and one signal generated from two equivalent CH_3 groups. Option (b) is the only spectrum with the correct number of signals.

13.44

^{1}H-NMR:

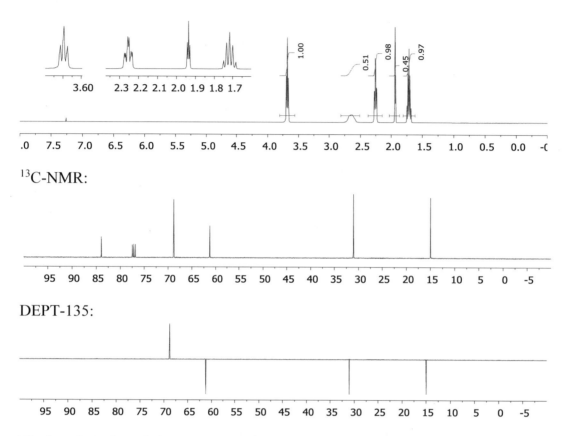

^{13}C-NMR:

DEPT-135:

The broad singlet at 2.6 ppm suggests that this structure is an alcohol or an amine. The two-hydrogen triplet represents the bold hydrogen in a fragment, suggesting that this is an alcohol, not an amine. There are two other two-hydrogen signals, likely CH_2 groups, a pentet, and a doublet of triplets. The pentet is between two other CH_2s, which, overlapping with the first fragment and the alcohol, gives $-CH_2-CH_2-CH_2-OH$. The remaining signal is a one-hydrogen triplet coupled to the last CH_2. According to the DEPT-135, there are three CH_2 carbons, which supports the integration from the ^{1}H-NMR.

The remaining hydrogen from the ^{1}H-NMR is the CH at 84 ppm. Typically, the carbon farthest downfield in the alkyl region is bonded to oxygen; however, hydrogen on that carbon is relatively upfield in the ^{1}H-NMR, less than 2 ppm. It is the carbon at 61 ppm that is the CH_2–O. Looking at Table 6.3, the other carbon types around 80 ppm are nitrile and alkyne carbons from 65 to 90 ppm. Nitriles do not have any CH, but a terminal alkyne does. That also explains the remaining carbon at 69 ppm that is missing in the DEPT-135. The structure is 4-pentyn-1-ol.

The signal at 2.25 ppm is a doublet of triplets because it couples to the adjacent CH_2 *and* to the alkyne CH. The alkyne CH is farther away than the three bonds usually required for coupling. Because this is a rigid system, coupling is possible 4 to 5 bonds away.

13.45

Both carveol and carvone have two alkenes, one of which has two hydrogens and one that has one hydrogen. Spectrum (a) and spectrum (b) each have one two-hydrogen multiplet at 4.7 ppm. These multiplets are likely the sp^2 hydrogens from the isopropenyl group. The one hydrogen on the ring alkene appears at 5.5 ppm in spectrum (a), and 6.7 ppm in spectrum (b). Spectrum (a) has signals between 4 and 4.5 ppm that are missing in spectrum (b). These signals can correspond to the CH adjacent to the oxygen and the OH signal in carveol. They disappear when the alcohol is oxidized. Also, the ketone in carvone is electron-withdrawing, which shifts the alkene CH farther downfield in spectrum (b).

a)

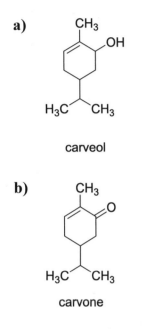

carveol

b)

CH₃

carvone

Chapter 14
Structure Determination II:
Mass Spectrometry and Infrared Spectroscopy

PROBLEMS

14.11

a) $M^+ = 56$, with an M+1 ^{13}C peak. M–1 is the most common fragment.

b) $M^+ = 58$, with an M+1 ^{13}C peak. The most common fragment is 29.

c) $M^+ = 120$, with an M+2 Cl peak. The most common fragment is 77.

d) $M^+ = 171$, with an M+2 Br peak and ^{13}C peaks. The biggest fragment is *m/e* 92.

e) $M^+ = 122$, with an M+2 Cl peak and ^{13}C peaks. Most common fragment is at me 43.

14.13

a) 2. The major fragment at 81 is a loss of CH_3; therefore, this is not the aldehyde.

b) 3. The mass of 97 identifies this compound.

c) 4. The mass of 98 identifies this compound.

d) 1. This must be the aldehyde, since (a) was matched to spectrum 2. There is nothing particularly characteristic upon which to make this determination otherwise.

14.15

a) Ethanol has an O–H stretching absorbance that diethyl ether does not.

b) The signals for O–H and N–H stretching appear in the same location but have different appearances. The N–H stretch is narrower and sharper than the O–H stretch, and two bands are observed for primary amines (RNH_2).

c) Both compounds have alkyl C–H stretch and C=O signals. The aldehyde has the characteristic Fermi doublet at 2700 and 2850 cm^{-1}.

d) These two compounds would have the same functional group absorbances, alkyl C–H, C=O, and C–O–C stretches. Differences would be found in the fingerprint region, and the two could be differentiated by comparing them to a standard spectrum of known compounds.

14.17

a)   4. The C=O stretch at 1730 cm^{-1} is not enough to distinguish between (a) and (d), but the C–O–C regions suggest 2 is an ether (1120 cm^{-1}) and 4 is an ester (1240 cm^{-1}). This characterization is advanced and could be misinterpreted, so the spectra should be compared to authentic spectra for confirmation.

b)   1. There is a characteristic OH stretch at 3400 cm^{-1}.

c)   3. There is a charactersitc CO$_2$H hydrogen-bonded O–H stretch at 2400 to 3400 cm^{-1}.

d)   2. See (a) for an explanation.

14.19

The compound is butanone. M$^+$ is 72. Fragments at 57 (the loss of 15 is a CH$_3$) and 43 (base; corresponds to COCH$_3^+$) suggest a C=OCH$_3$. A loss of 28 (CO) from 57 (RC=O$^+$) leaves 29, which corresponds to an ethyl cation (CH$_3$CH$_2^+$). The IR spectrum shows alkyl C–H and a C=O, with no indication of any other O or any N. C=O has a mass of 28, leaving a remaining mass of 44, which is C$_3$H$_8$. Three saturated alkyl carbons with a carbonyl can only be either butanal or butanone. The absence of aldehyde C–H stretches suggests butanone.

14.21

The M$^+$ = 76. The strong M+2 shows the presence of Cl, leaving a remaining mass of 41. The IR spectrum shows a C=C stretch and no indication of any oxygen, with no C=O, C–O–C, or O–H signals. The remaining mass is C$_3$H$_5$. This could be either 2-chloropropene or 3-chloropropene (allyl chloride). There is no reliable way to distinguish between these compounds without comparison to a library spectrum or a thorough analysis of the MS fragmentation. The MS fragmentation analysis is: if this 1-chloropropene, one would expect to see a (M–CH$_3$)$^+$ peak at 61 with a 30% 63 peak, due to the presence of Cl. This peak is absent. Therefore, this compound must be 3-chloropropene (allyl chloride).

14.23

The MS shows the highest mass peak at 164. The IR has a strong signal near 1050 cm^{-1}, suggesting a C–O–C. There is no evidence of a C=O (the band at 1720 is too weak to be a carbonyl stretch), meaning the C–O–C would be an ether, not an ester. The ^{1}H-NMR has two ^{2}H aromatic signals, suggesting that there is a *p*-substituted benzene ring. The remaining signals have integrations of 1, 4, 2, 2, 2, 6, and 3 Hs, with coupling of singlet, quartet, triplet, pentet, sextet, triplet, and triplet. The one H signal near 6.3 cannot be an OH signal, since there is no O–H stretch in the IR.

The 4H quartet must be two symmetrical CH$_2$ groups, each bonded to a CH$_3$. The 6H triplet must be two symmetrical CH$_3$ groups, each bonded to a CH$_2$. This suggests the presence of two equivalent ethyl groups. The chemical shift of the 4H quartet suggests that the CH$_2$s are each bonded to an oxygen atom, making two equivalent ethoxy groups. They may be each bonded to a CH, consistent with the one H singlet near 6 ppm. The splitting patterns of the remaining alkyl signals [2H (triplet), 2H (pentet), 2H (hextet), 3H (triplet)] suggest CH$_2$CH$_2$CH$_2$CH$_3$.

This gives the following C and H fragments:

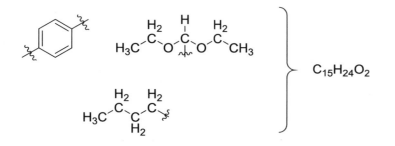

$$C_{15}H_{24}O_2$$

The mass of C$_{15}$H$_{24}$O$_2$ is 236; therefore, the mass spectrum did not identify the M$^+$ ion. This provides a DU of 4. Since the phenyl group accounts for a DU of 4, the rest of the molecule must have no π bond or ring.

The butyl group must be one end of the molecule. The symmetrical ethoxy groups must be the other end, with the benzene ring in the middle. The chemical shifts of the CH group [5.9 ppm, (s)] and one CH$_2$ group [2.55 ppm, (t)] are consistent with these connections.

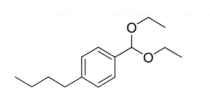

14.25

The MS shows $M^+ = 121$, which suggests that there is nitrogen present.

The IR has a strong signal near 1710 cm^{-1}, suggesting a C=O. The signal near 1300 cm^{-1} suggests a possible ester C–O–C.

The ^{1}H-NMR has four aromatic signals, each with one H, and a signal representing CH$_3$. The ^{13}C-NMR has only five aromatic carbons, one carbon for a carbonyl, and one alkyl carbon. The five aromatic carbons suggest a pyridine with one substituent.

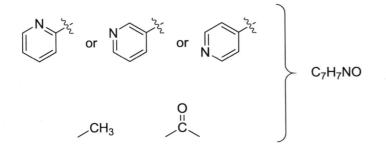

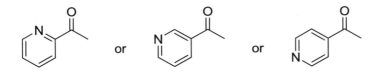

The mass of these fragments account for the entire mass of 121, which eliminates the possibility of an ester C–O–C fragment.

These fragments can be assembled into three possible structures.

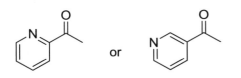

The four ^{1}H-NMR and five ^{13}C-NMR aromatic signals indicate that the ring is not symmetrical, eliminating the last structure, 4-acetylpyridine. The remaining 2-acetyl and 3-acetyl isomers cannot be easily distinguished without better resolution spectra that show coupling information.

MCAT Style Problems

14.27

Answer (a). The $M^+ = 160$, indicating either no nitrogens or an even number of nitrogens. There are no M+2 signals, indicating no chlorine or bromine. This eliminates options (b) and (c). Option (d) has a mass of 164, not 160. Option (a) is the only structure with a mass of 160 and no chlorine.

14.29

Answer (d). The IR does not show any evidence of a C=O, eliminating options (a) and (c). There is an alcohol O–H, consistent with options (b) and (d). There is also a small C≡C stretch near 2200 cm^{-1} and an sp C–H stretch at 3300 cm^{-1}. This is consistent with option (d) and eliminates option (b).

Challenge Problem

14.30

Product C $\xleftarrow[\text{2) NH}_4\text{Cl, H}_2\text{O}]{\text{1) NaBH}_4}$ Compound A $\xrightarrow[\text{AlCl}_3]{\text{Cl}_2}$ Product B

Compound A has a pair of doublets in the ^{1}H-NMR, at 7.82 and 7.52 ppm, a molecular ion peak at m/z = 140 and an M+2 peak at 142. This corresponds to either a chloride or a bromide.

The IR for compound A suggests an aldehyde, with C=O near 1700 cm^{-1} and aldehyde C–H Fermi doublet absorbance between 2700 and 2900 cm^{-1}. The ^{1}H-NMR signals suggest a *para*-substituted aromatic ring. The mass of an aldehyde and a benzene ring gives mass of 105 and a remaining mass of 35. The remaining mass and the M+2 peak are consistent with a chlorine.

Compound A:

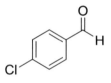

Product B is a result of chlorination of an aromatic ring. The addition of a second chlorine will happen at carbon 3, *ortho* to the original chlorine. This is because the Cl is an electron-donating group and activates *ortho/para*. The carbonyl is *meta*-directing, reinforcing the chloride driven selectivity *ortho* to itself.

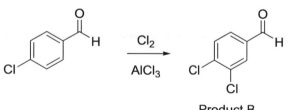

Product B

Product C is an alcohol, as shown by the IR spectrum. Addition of a hydride reduces an aldehyde to an alcohol.

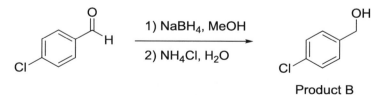

Product B

Chapter 15
π Bond Electrophiles Connected to Leaving Groups:
Carboxylic Acid Derivatives and Their Reactions

PROBLEMS

15.25

a) Amide → carboxylic acid **can** be done directly.

Amides can be hydrolyzed to carboxylic acids with acid catalysis in excess water.

b) Acid chloride → ester **can** be done directly.

When adding a nucleophile to make a tetrahedral intermediate, the intermediate collapses to eliminate the better leaving group. In general, leaving group ability decreases in this order:

chloride > anhydride > ester ≈ carboxylic acid > amide > carboxylate salt

The better leaving group is eliminated to form the desired product.

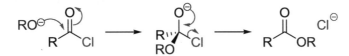

c) Ester → anhydride **cannot** be done directly.

d) Ester → carboxylic acid **can** be done directly.

Esters can be hydrolyzed to carboxylic acids with acid catalysis in excess water.

e) Anhydride → amide **can** be done directly

See part (b); the explanation is also pertinent here.

f) Carboxylic acid → amide **cannot** be done directly.

The nucleophile required to form an amide from a carboxylic acid (an amine) is too basic and will deprotonate the acid to form the less-reactive carboxylate salt. A carboxylate will not form an amide under typical reaction conditions.

15.27

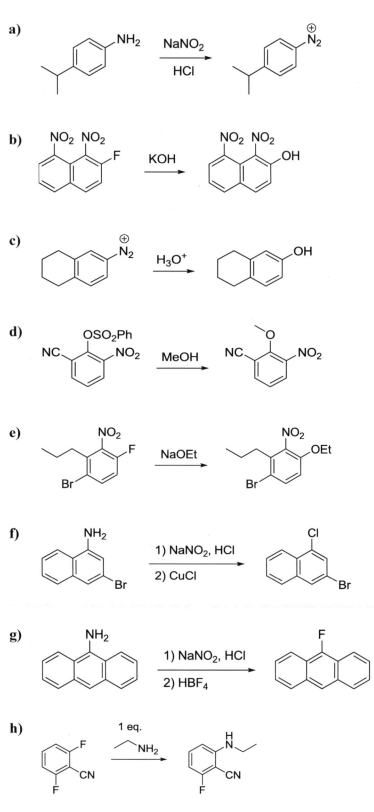

15.29

When adding a neutral amine as a nucleophile to an acid chloride, HCl will be generated as a by-product of the reaction. Unless there is enough base to react with the extra acid, half of the amine nucleophile will end up protonated. In the protonated state, it cannot act as a nucleophile and the reaction cannot proceed with more than 50 percent yield.

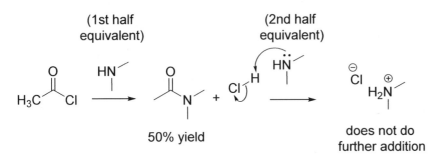

15.31

Desacetyl matricarin is type of lactone known as a *guaianolide* because of the 5-7-5-membered ring system. Aqueous acid hydrolyzes the ester shown in **bold** to form a free acid. Removal of water shifts the equilibrium back towards an ester; however, there are now two alcohols that may react. The other alcohol indicated in the figure can form a new guaianolide, with a new five-membered ring lactone.

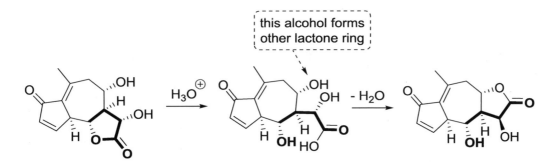

15.33

After a hydroxide attacks the carbonyl to form a tetrahedral intermediate, it collapses to eliminate the best leaving group. The presence of three bromides stabilizes the negative charge on carbon enough that it is a better leaving group than hydroxide. After it is eliminated to form a carboxylic acid, it acts as a base to remove the acidic proton and form bromoform.

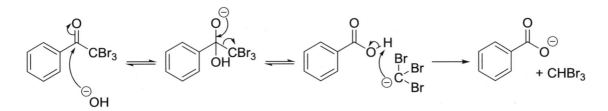

15.35

Aspirin synthesis:

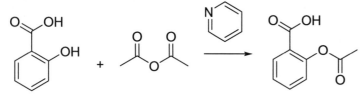

15.37

Nitro group **C** is both *ortho* and *para* to another electron-withdrawing group; thus, it is the most activated for substitution. Nitros **A** and **B** are either *ortho* or *para* to another, so they are half as activated as **C**.

15.39

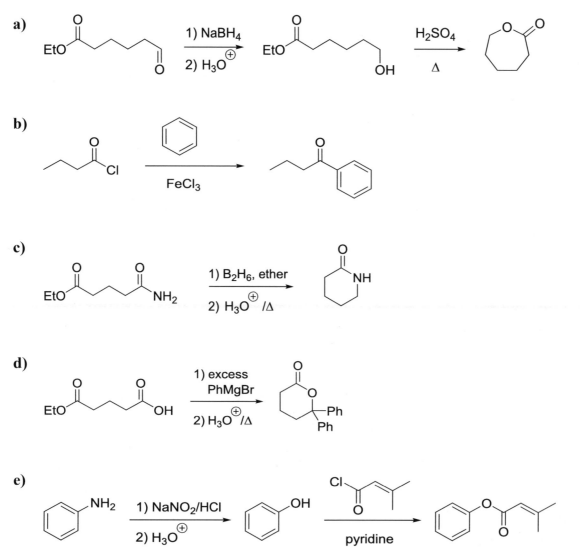

f)

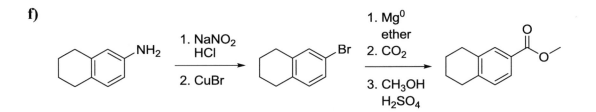

15.41

a) A mechanism for the formation of TCPO and its reaction with hydrogen peroxide:

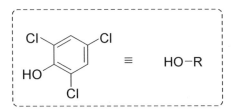

TCPO formation

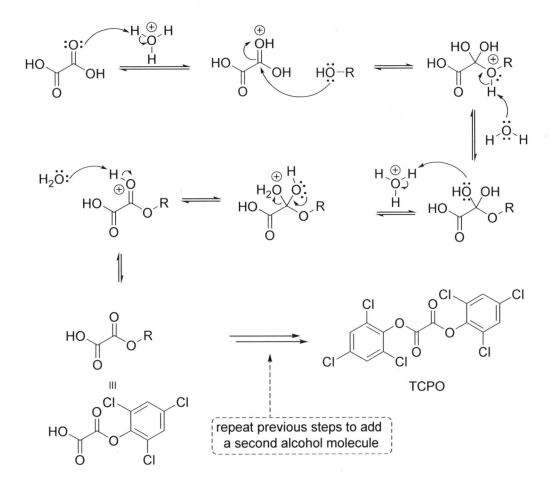

Peroxide addition:

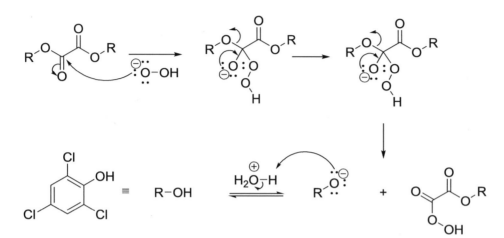

Ring formation:

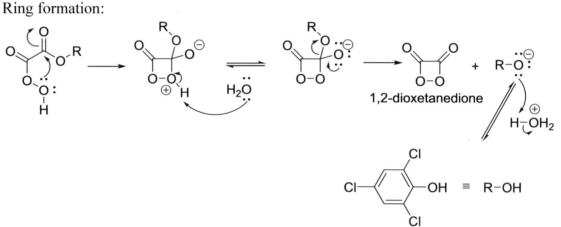

b) The standard line drawing of TCPO suggests that the structure is flat, with the aromatic rings in the same plane as the ester carbonyls. Being planar allows conjugation between the aromatic rings and the ester.

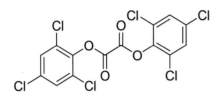

However, the chlorines are too large to avoid overlapping with the carbonyl oxygens, and the lowest energy conformation has the rings almost 90° to the plane of the carbonyls, preventing conjugation. Since conjugation lowers the energy of molecules, TCPO has higher energy than expected.

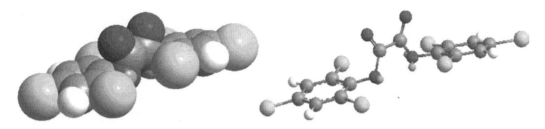

c) Dioxetane has high ring strain, which contributes to a high heat of formation of 64.53 kcal/mol. The heat of formation of carbon dioxide gas is –95.05 kJ/mol. A large downhill difference between the products and starting materials is usually released as heat. With the help of a fluorophore, in this case the energy is released as light.

15.43

a) The hydroxyisobutyl group could come from the reduction of a ketone, which can be made using the Friedel-Crafts acylation. The ketone directs *meta*, which allows for the placement of a hydroxyl group via diazonium salt substitution.

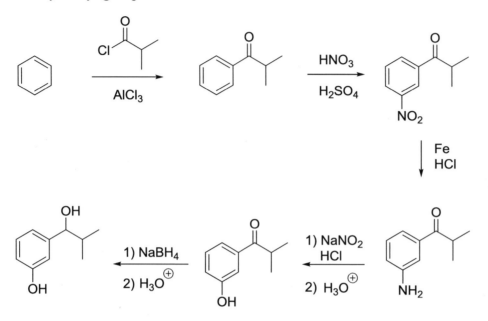

b) There are several ways this compound could be made. One way is to make a Grignard reagent to attack benzaldehyde.

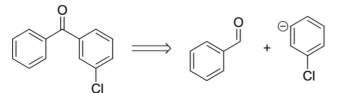

Grignard synthesis via nitro group gives *meta* regiochemistry. Iodides form Grignards more readily than chlorides and so give selective formation of the Grignard.

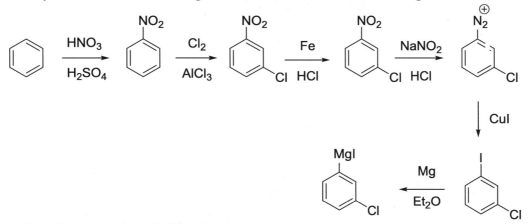

Aldehyde synthesis and alkylation:

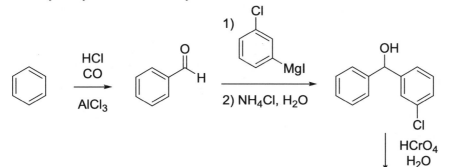

c) Both substituents on this ring can be added using S$_E$Ar reactions from Chapter 10. The amide substituent on this ring is electron-donating and directs incoming electrophiles *ortho/para*. The acyl substituent is electron-withdrawing and directs *meta*. Therefore, the amide nitrogen must be added before the acyl group in order to achieve the desired *para* substituted product. The formation of the amide, using an addition-elimination reaction with acetyl chloride and pyridine increases the steric hindrance and prevents significant *ortho* substitution during the Friedel-Crafts acylation step.

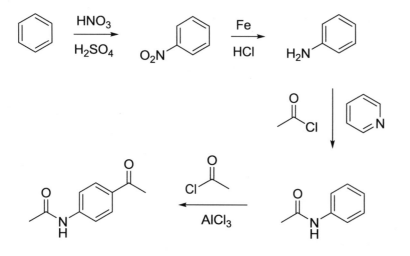

d) There are a number of ways to make this compound, also. Adding the large phenyl ester blocks the *ortho* position to the nitro group adds *para*.

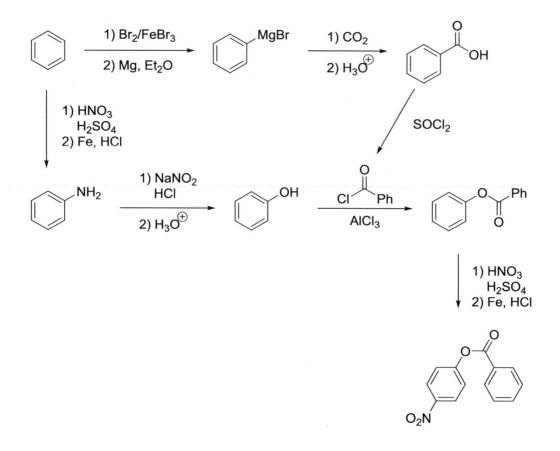

MCAT Style Problems

15.45

Answer: (b). Ester hydrolysis produces a carboxylic acid and an alcohol. The passage states that pancreatic lipase hydrolyzes two of the three esters, which would produce two long-chain carboxylates and two hydroxyl groups on the remaining lipid fragment. Therefore, answer (b) is correct.

Challenge Problem

15.47

Acid derivatives that can form ketones must have some way to prevent collapse of the tetrahedral intermediate to eliminate the leaving group. If this happens too early, the resulting ketone will be attacked a second time by remaining Grignard reagents. If there is another functional group that can help coordinate to a positive ion in a five- or six-membered ring, it may be possible at low temperatures to prevent the electrons on the negative oxygen from re-forming a carbonyl. Once water is added to neutralize the Grignard reagent, elimination can then occur without danger of another addition.

a)

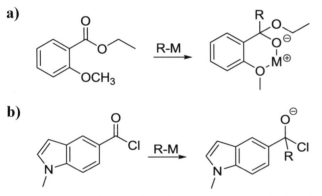

b)

No second coordinating group is available to stabilize the intermediate.

c)

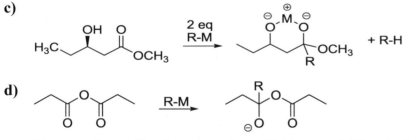

d)

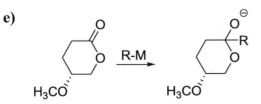

No second coordinating group is available to stabilize the intermediate.

e)

No second coordinating group is available to stabilize the intermediate.

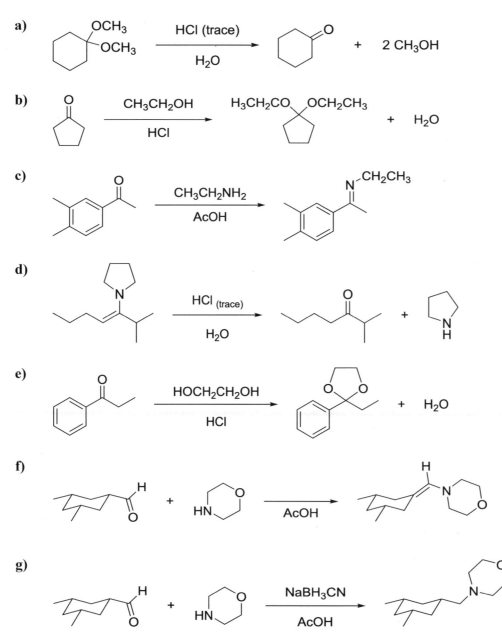

Chapter 16
π Bonds with Hidden Leaving Groups:
Reactions of Acetals and Related Compounds

PROBLEMS

16.13

a)

b)

c)

d)

e)

f)

g)

h)

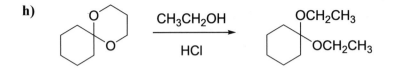

16.15

a) Both five- and six-membered hemiacetals can form. The six-membered ring is generally favoured in cyclization reactions.

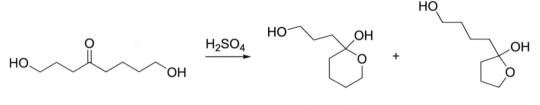

major product

b) Amine will be protonated under strong acid and become unreactive.

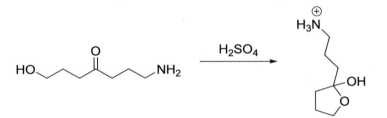

c) Under weak acid conditions, the imine can form.

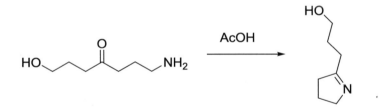

d) Stereochemistry on the ester groups is retained in the product.

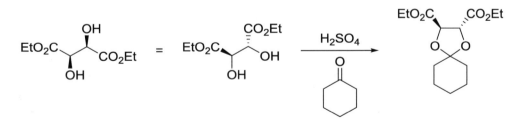

e) The reagent is a masked source of ethoxide.

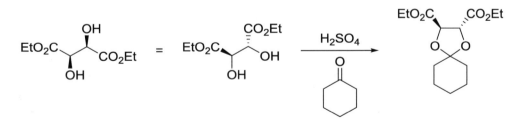

16.17

a)

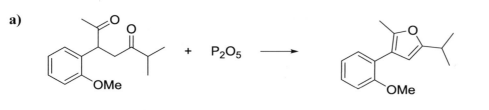

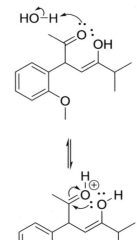

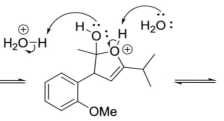

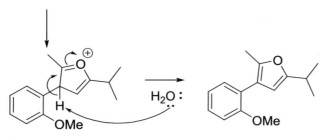

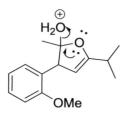

b)

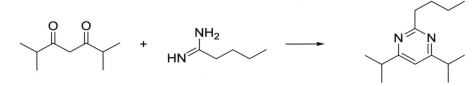

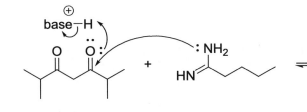

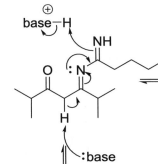

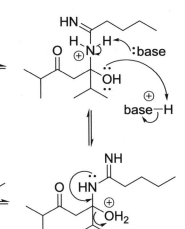

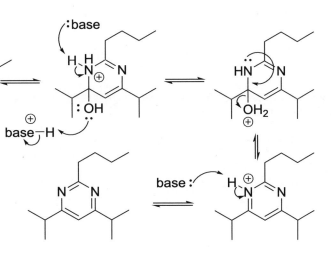

c)

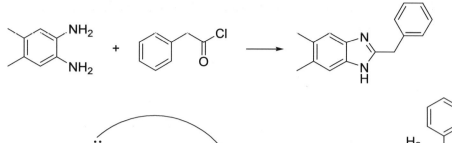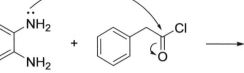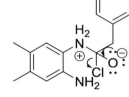

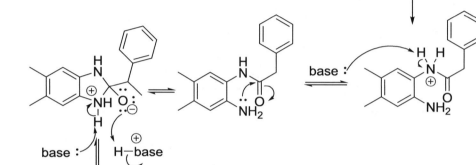

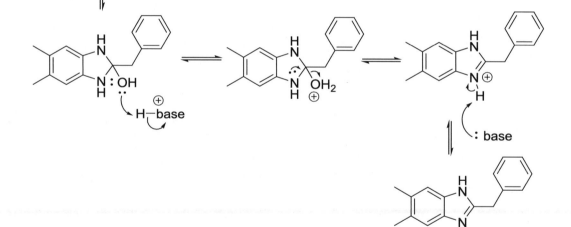

d) Cyclization would give a seven-membered ring and no resonance stabilization, so oximes form instead.

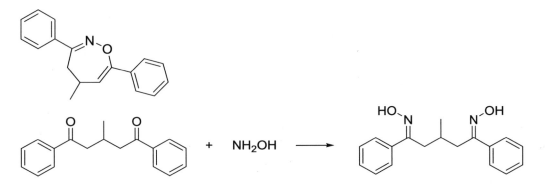

16.19

a) 2 $H_2^{18}O$ ⇌ $H_3^{18}O^{\oplus}$ + $^{18}OH^{\ominus}$

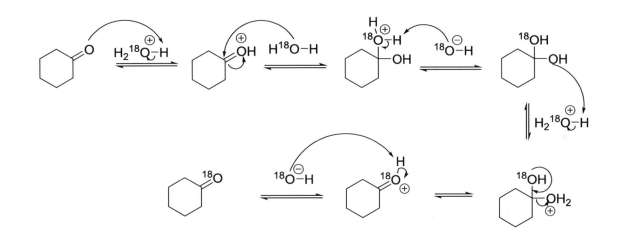

b) The hemiacetal is the site that would be reactive with labelled water. The label is introduced by first producing the aldehyde incorporating the label. Reforming the hemiacetal produces the original molecule with a labelled oxygen.

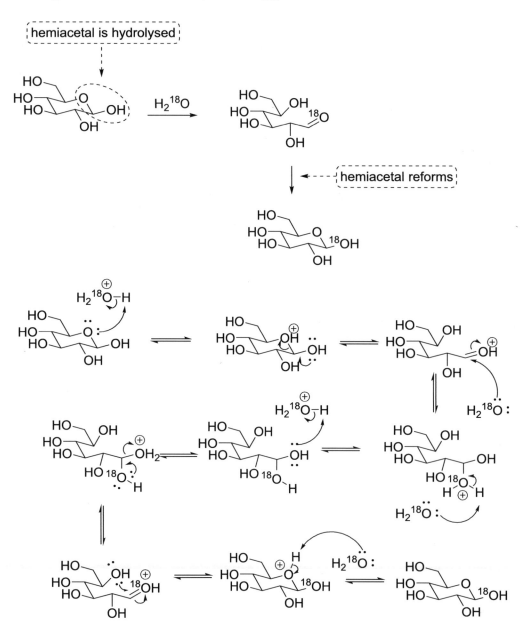

c) There are two sites that can react and introduce labelled oxygen from the water: an acetal and a hemiacetal. The hemiacetal exchanges more quickly because it only requires the formation of an oxonium intermediate to exchange the OH group. The acetal requires a ring-opening step before the OH group produced in the ring opening can exchange. These reactions can then be reversed to reconstitute the original molecule with labelled oxygen.

Hemiacetal exchange:

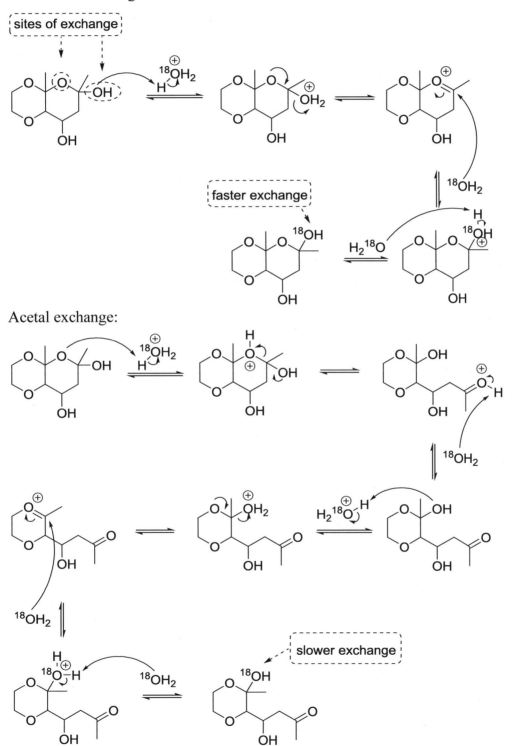

Acetal exchange:

16.21

The acetone is activated by protonation of the carbonyl.

Acetone activation

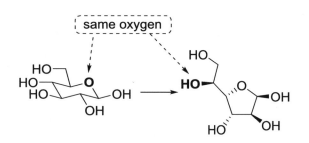

Under acidic conditions, there can be an isomerization of the ring to a five-membered form via the hemiacetal opening and reforming with a different hydroxyl group.

The formation of the two acetal linkages now occurs at the two diol groupings.

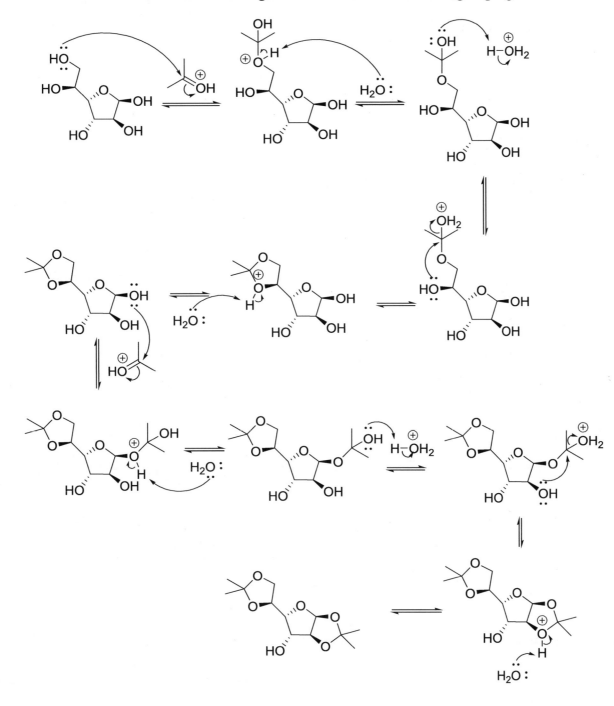

The 2,3 diol grouping does not react, due to the *trans* stereochemistry of the hydroxyl groups.

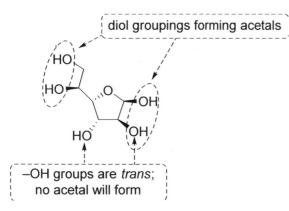

16.23

a)

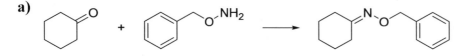

b) The acetal can hydrolyse to an aldehyde.

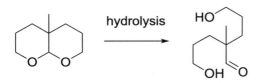

This then reacts to form the final product.

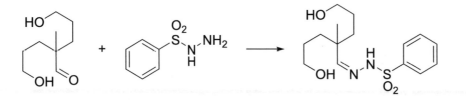

c) The acetal groups can hydrolyse to form formaldehyde and a ketone.

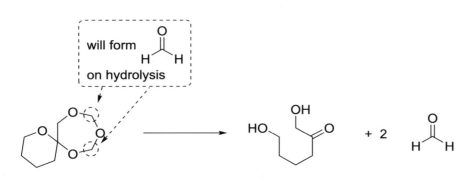

The ketone then reacts with the hydrazine to form a hydrazone.

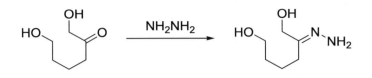

16.25

a) Zinc chloride acts as an acid to activate the carbonyl to nucleophilic attack.

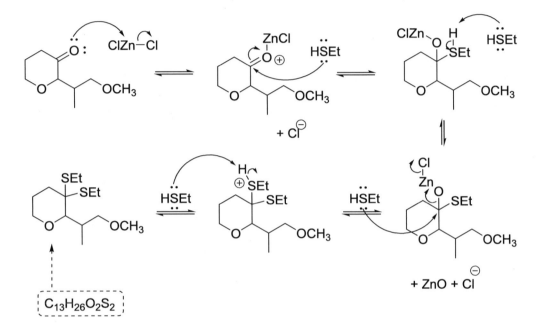

b)

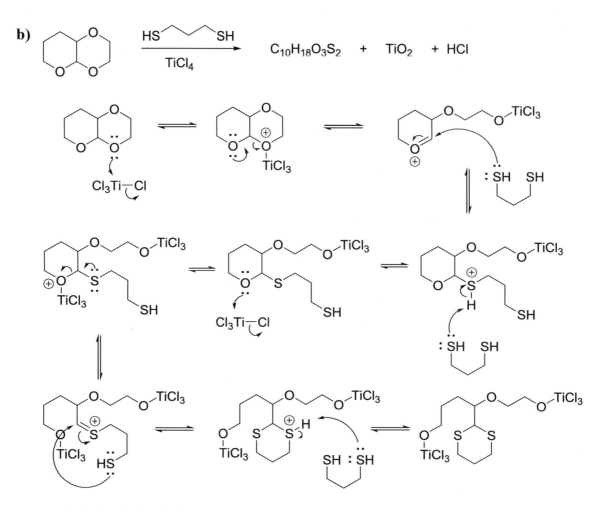

Hydrolysis of the final product would release the alcohol groups.

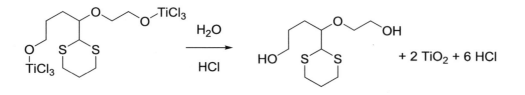

16.27

a)

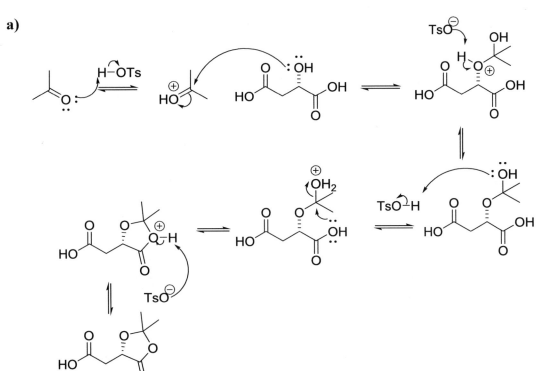

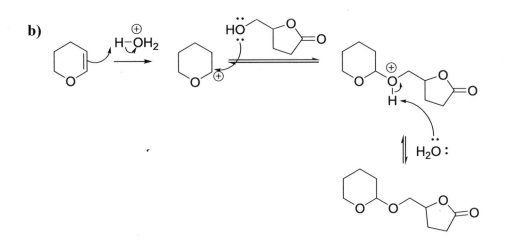

b)

c)

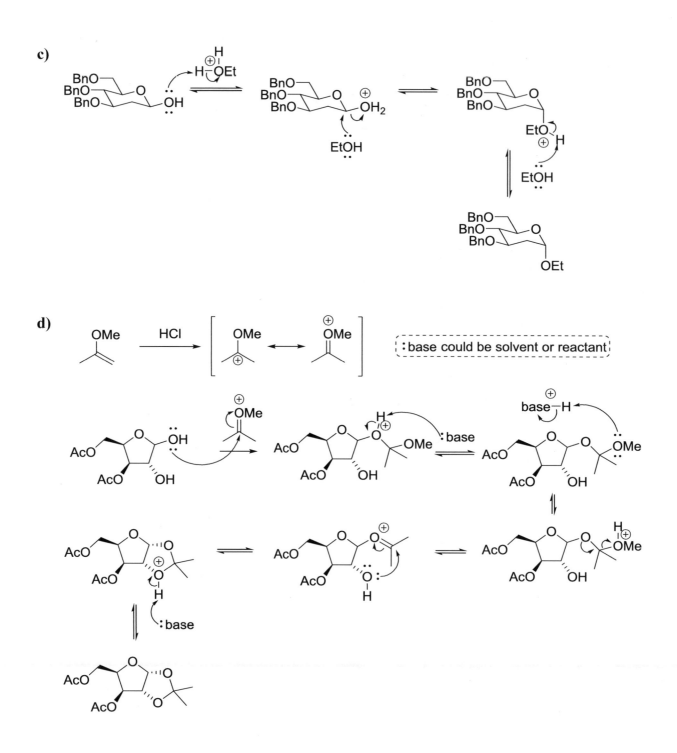

d)

Copyright © 2018 Nelson Education Limited

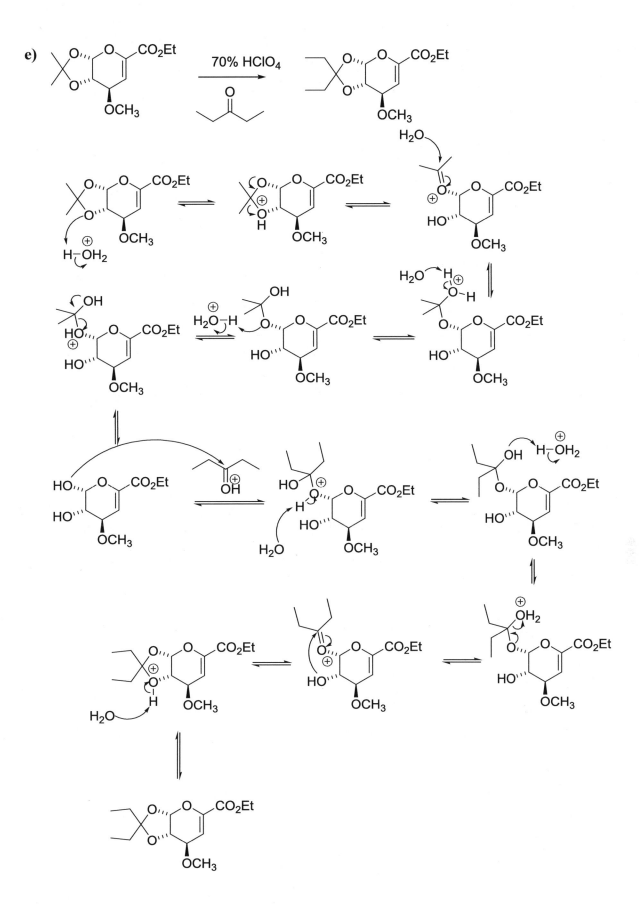

f)

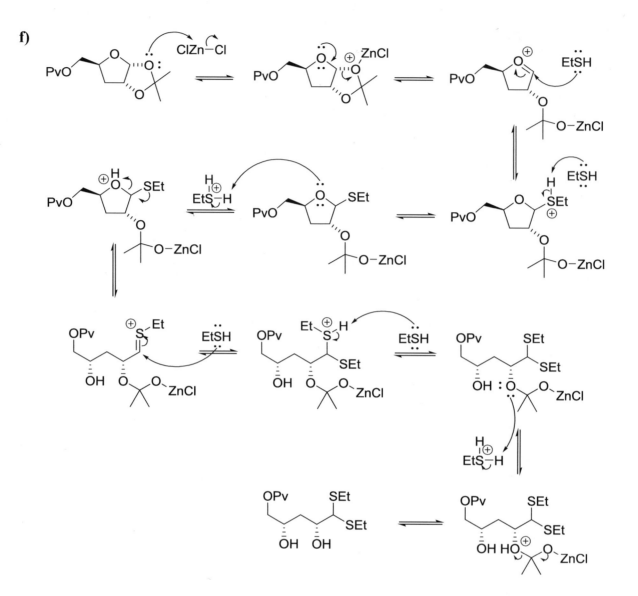

16.29

a)

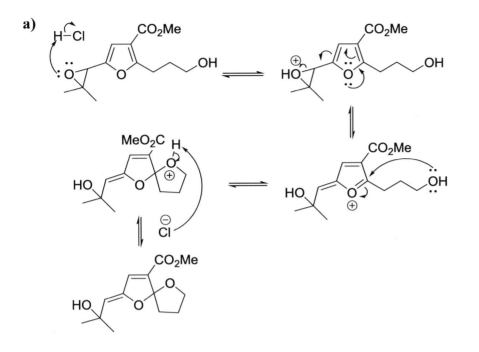

b)

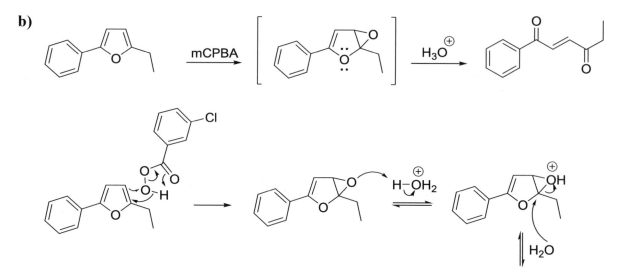

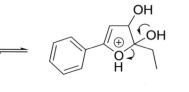

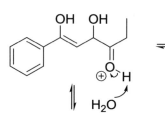

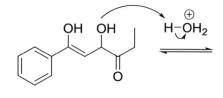

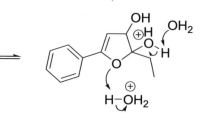

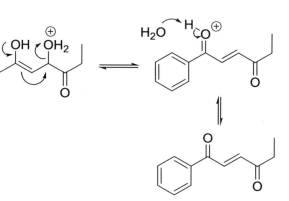

c)

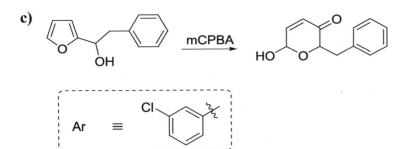

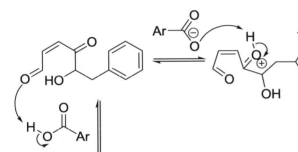

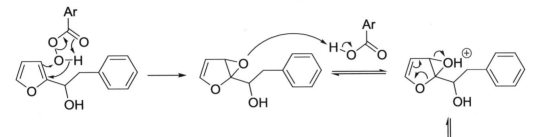

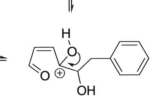

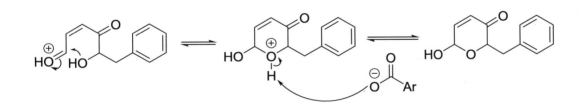

d) Step 1:

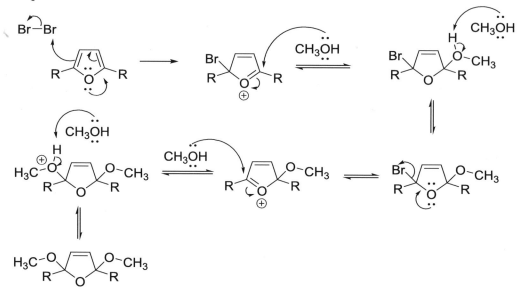

Step 2:

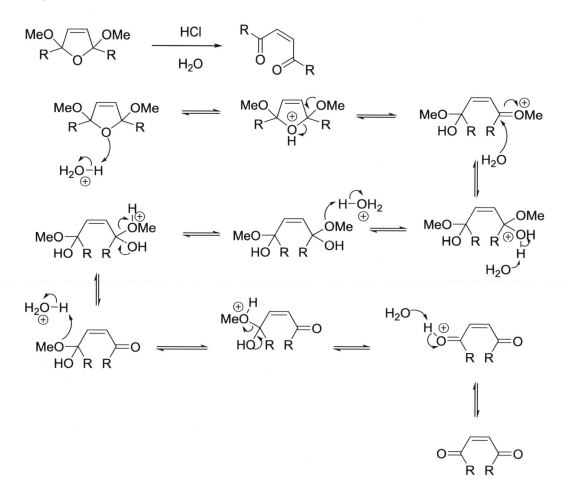

16.31

a)

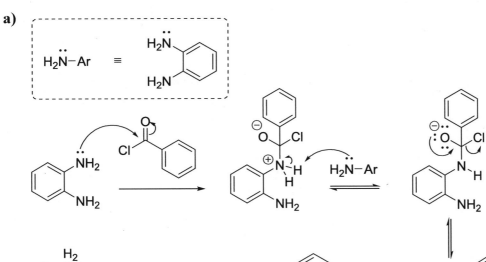

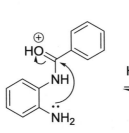

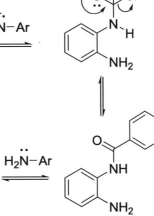

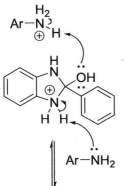

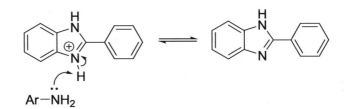

b) NaHSO₃:

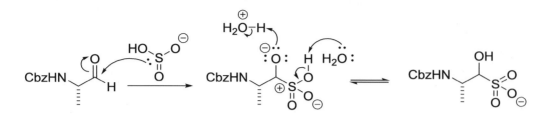

NaCN:

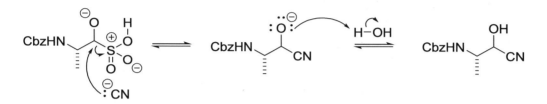

HCl, EtOH:

$$\rightleftharpoons$$

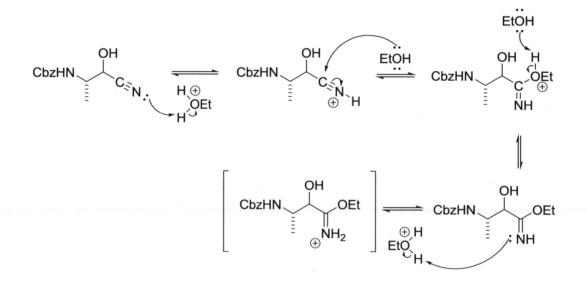

Ring formation:

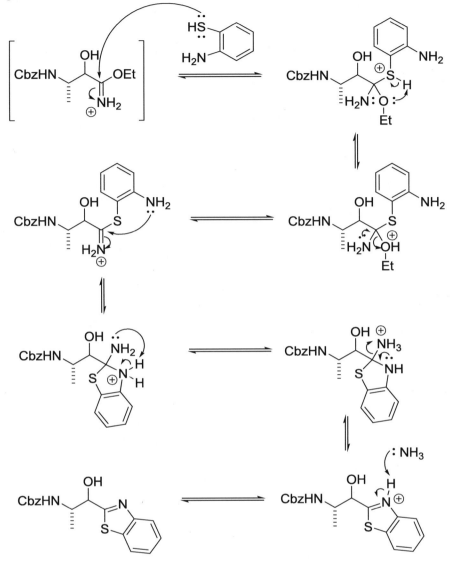

MCAT Style Problems

16.33

Answer :(c). A five-membered cyclic acetal will be formed.

16.35

Answer :(c).

Challenge Problem

16.36

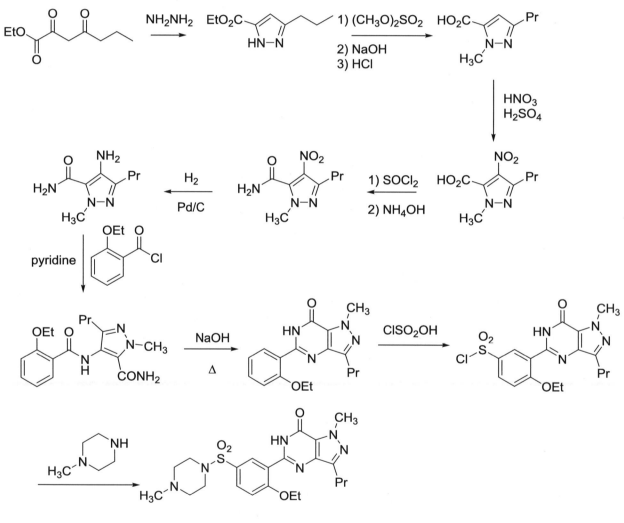

Viagra

Pyrazole formation:

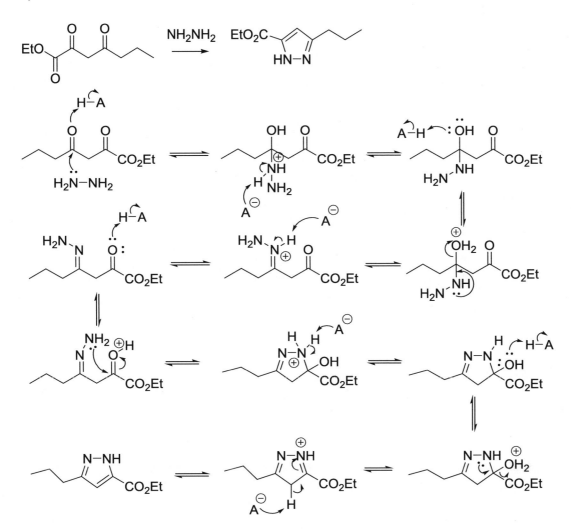

Methylation of nitrogen, hydrolysis of ester:

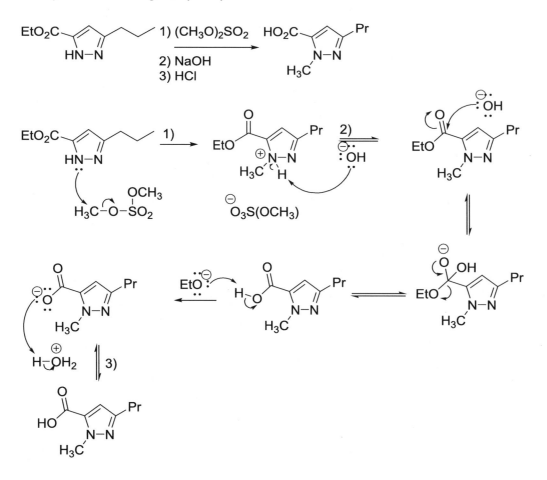

Nitration of aromatic ring:

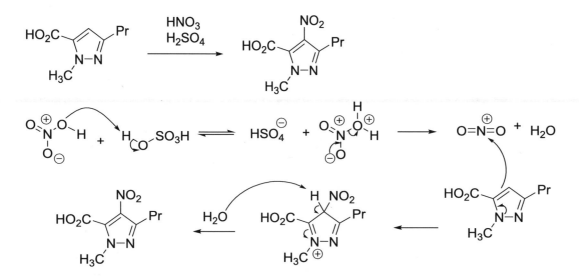

Amide formation via acid chloride:

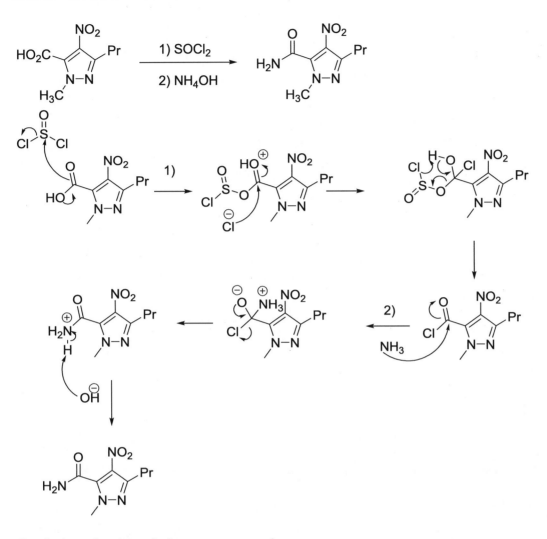

Catalytic reduction of nitro group to amine:

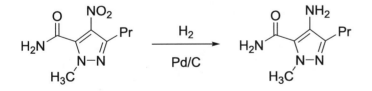

Amide formation:

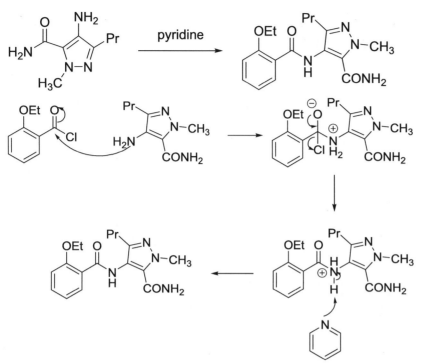

Cyclization of by coupling of amide groups:

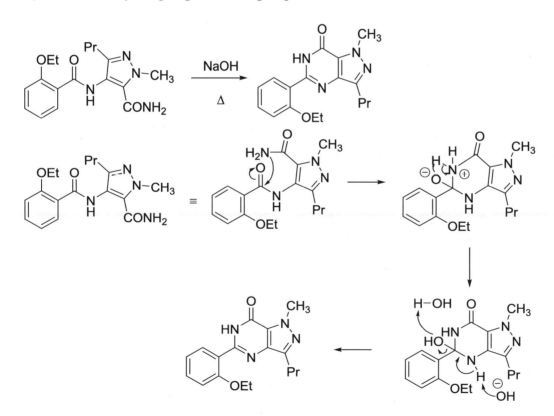

Aromatic substitution with SO2Cl:

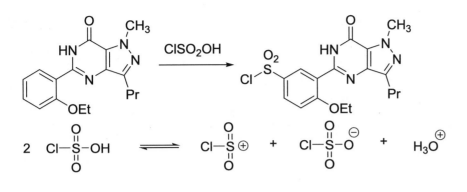

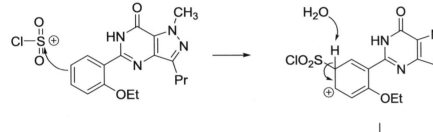

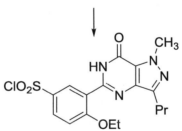

Alkylation of secondary amide:

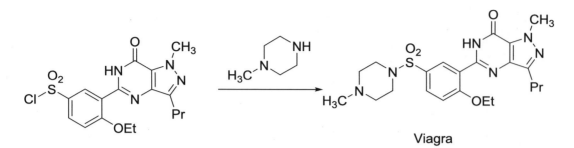

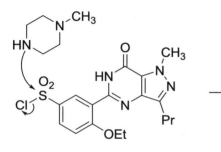

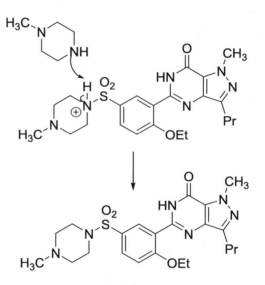

Chapter 17
Carbonyl-Based Nucleophiles:
The Aldol, Claisen, Wittig, and Related Enolate Reactions

PROBLEMS

17.39

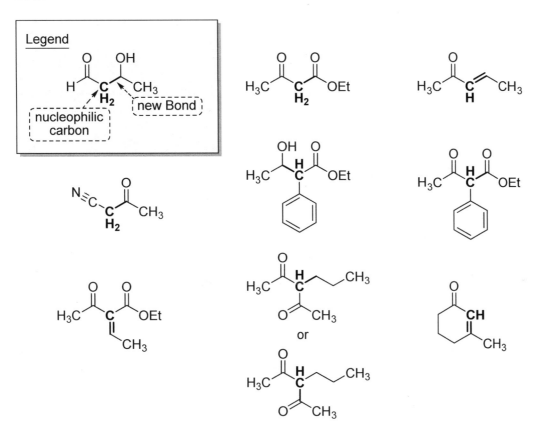

17.41

a)

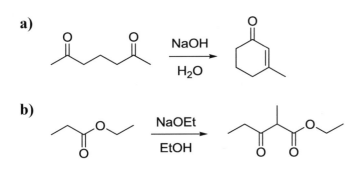

b)

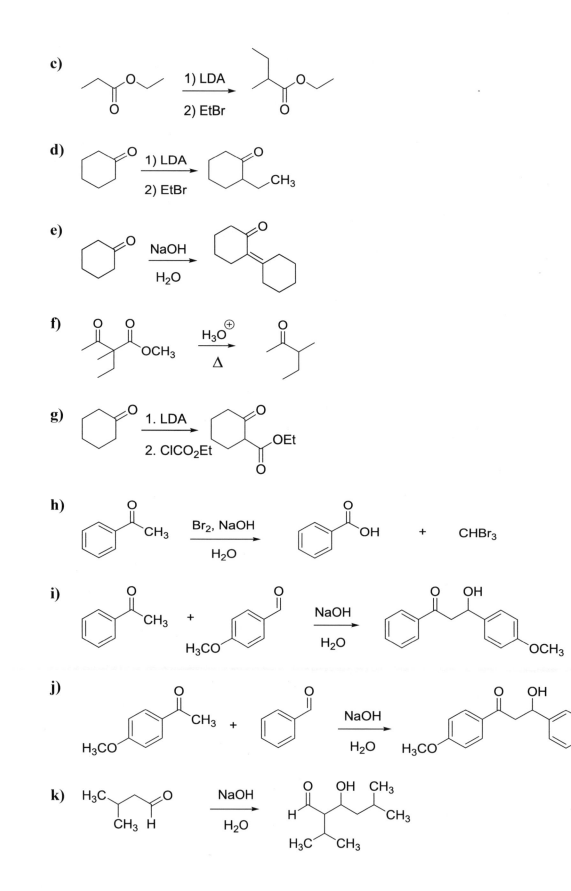

c)

d)

e)

f)

g)

h)

i)

j)

k)

l)

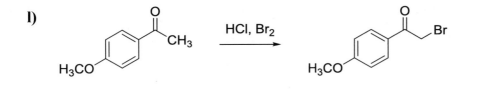

m)

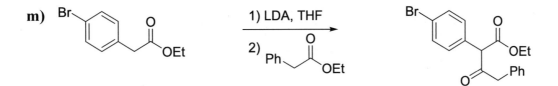

17.43

a)

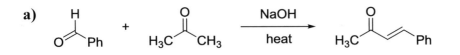

b)

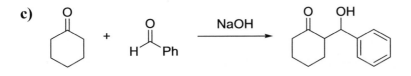

c)

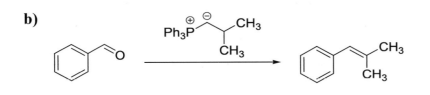

d)

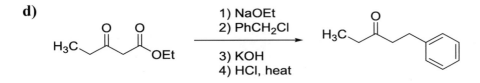

e)

 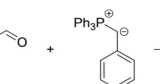 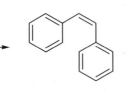

f)

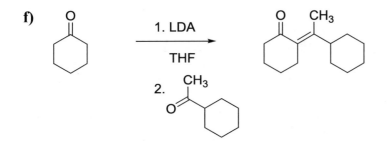

g)

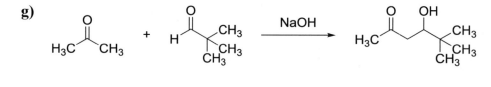

h)

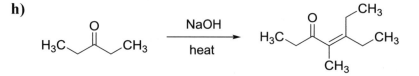

i)

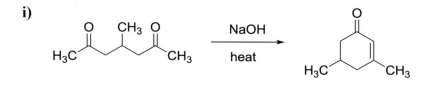

j)

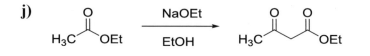

17.45

a)

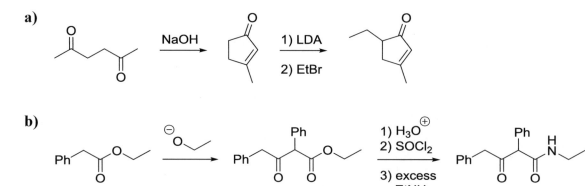

b)

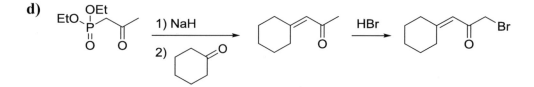

c)

d)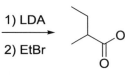

e)

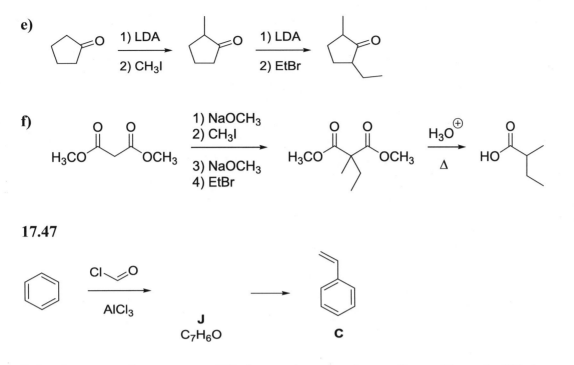

f)

17.47

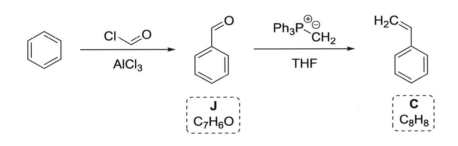

It is often more direct to use a Wittig reaction to make an alkene. Since the Wittig reaction adds a carbon, the Friedel-Crafts step must add one less carbon.

17.49

The mechanism is an aldol condensation between acetone and one carbonyl of the 1,2-diketone and an aldol addition with the other acetone alpha carbon and the second ketone.

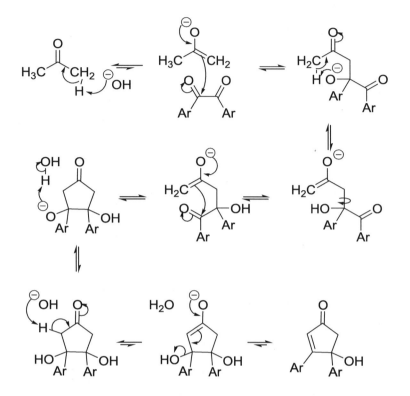

Introducing sp^2 carbons into a ring often increases angle strain because it reduces the flexibility needed to adopt a more stable conformation. The first elimination to form a cyclopentenone increases conjugation, which lowers the overall energy more than the increase in angle strain, due to the addition of one double bond. A second elimination would form a cyclopentadienone. The decreased flexibility of having *all* the carbons in the ring sp^2-hybridized will cause an increase in angle strain that cannot be offset by the increase in conjugation of adding a second double bond.

17.51

The five-membered ring is formed by an enolate formed on carbon 3 condensing with the second carbonyl on carbon 7.

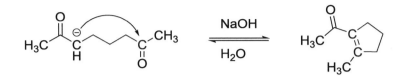

The seven-membered ring would be formed by an enolate formed on carbon 1 condensing with the carbonyl on carbon 7.

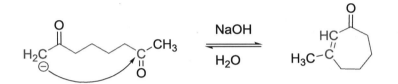

The ring strain energy of five-membered rings is lower than the strain in seven-membered rings. Because each step of the aldol condensation is reversible, the lowest energy (most stable) product is formed preferentially. Higher-energy products that are in equilibrium reverse to allow the formation of lower-energy products.

17.53

The condensation can be catalyzed by base, as shown below.

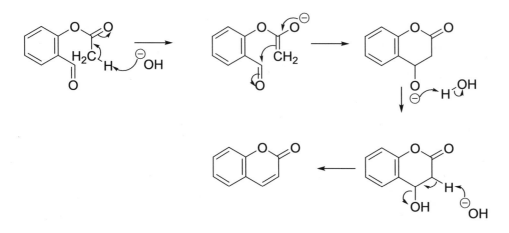

The mechanism could also be acid catalyzed, as shown below.

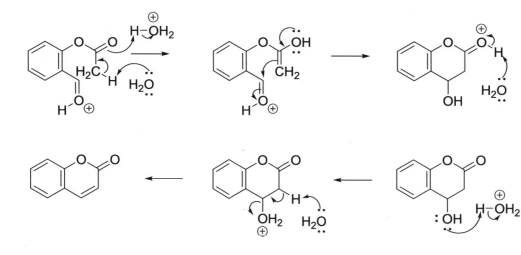

17.55

Since only one compound was reacted with a weak base, this reaction is some kind of self-addition or condensation. The ¹H-NMR of compound **A** shows three signals with integration of 1.5:1:1.5, which is more properly 3:2:3. The three-hydrogen singlet at 3.6 suggests a methyl ester. The other two signals, a two-hydrogen quartet and a three-hydrogen triplet appear to be an ethyl group. The ¹³C-NMR shows three alkyl carbons and one at 176 that could be an ester carbonyl. Compound **A** is methyl propanate. The reaction conditions are consistent with a Claisen condensation, which would yield the following product.

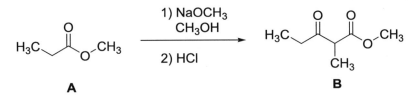

A   **B**

The ¹H-NMR of **B** still indicates a methyl ester and an ethyl group. The two new signals are a one-hydrogen quartet and a three-hydrogen doublet, consistent with the new CH–CH₃ group between the carbonyls. The ¹³C-NMR has the appropriate number of alkyl carbons and now shows the presence of a ketone carbonyl.

17.57

Alkyl triphenylphosphonium salts are used in the Wittig reaction to produce alkenes from ketones or aldehydes. The five aromatic hydrogens and the aldehyde hydrogen at 10 ppm in the ¹H-NMR indicate that compound **A** is benzaldehyde. Compound **B** has lost the aldehyde hydrogen and now shows two alkene hydrogens near 6 ppm. The other three signals at and below 2 ppm are a propyl group. The three new carbons from the propyl group are seen in the ¹³C-NMR below 30 ppm. This is all consistent with the use of a butyl phosphonium salt in the following reaction.

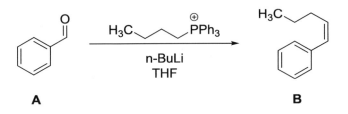

A   **B**

MCAT Style Problems

17.59

Answer: (d). The Haloform reaction can occur with methyl ketones. Butanone, compound (d), is the only methyl ketone listed.

17.61

Answer: (d). Statements II and III are correct. Hydroxide base deprotonates ketones only reversibly in an unfavourable equilibrium, unless there is a β-keto group. When deprotonation occurs, it occurs at the less-hindered side.

Challenge Problems

17.62

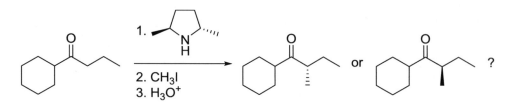

The first step forms a nucleophilic enamine. The steric hindrance between the alkyl chain of the ketone and the methyl from the pyrrolidine ring causes the equilibrium to favour the alkyl group appearing on the opposite side of the alkene from the nitrogen.

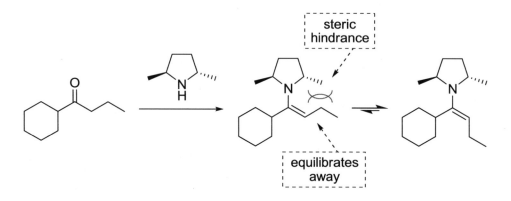

The methyl also blocks the approach of the electrophile from behind. This causes the methyl addition from the front to be favoured.

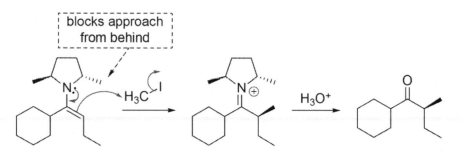

Rotation into the more standard zig-zag conformation moves the added methyl to the back. The addition of the methyl group pointing forward is disfavoured.

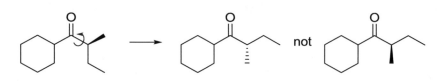

17.63

The half-chair conformation is often represented as a stylized "bow-tie" that resembles, but doesn't represent, the true shape of the cyclohexene. Shown below is a more accurate representation of the enolate viewed from the same angle as well as from slightly above the plane of the molecule.

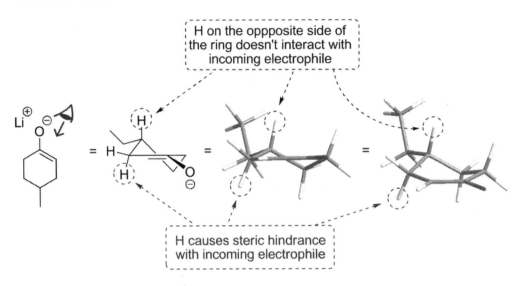

In these representations, it is easier to see that the carbon and hydrogen that point above the plane are on the opposite side of the ring from the enolate. Even though they look like they will block the approaching electrophile, it is in fact the hydrogen adjacent to the alkene that is in a "pseudo-axial" position and causes more steric hindrance. For the enantiomer shown, an electrophile will add from the top, not the bottom.

Chapter 18
Selectivity and Reactivity
in Organic Reactions:
Control of Stereoselectivity and Regioselectivity

PROBLEMS

18.21

All of the conjugate additions require a cuprate. All of the direct additions require Grignard reagents. Direct addition to esters initially produces a ketone, which is subject to a second addition to produce a tertiary alcohol. This requires at least two equivalents of ethylmagnesium bromide. The conjugate addition requires diethyl cuprate.

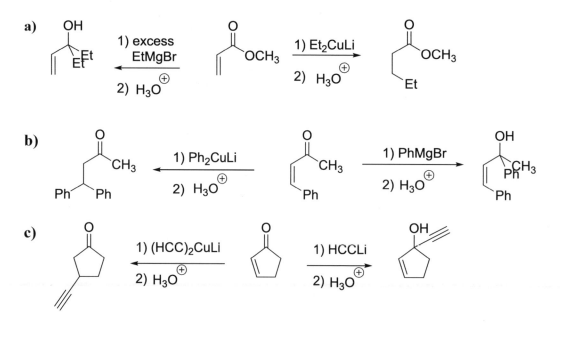

18.23

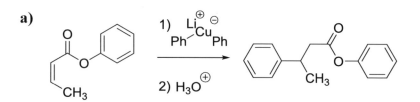

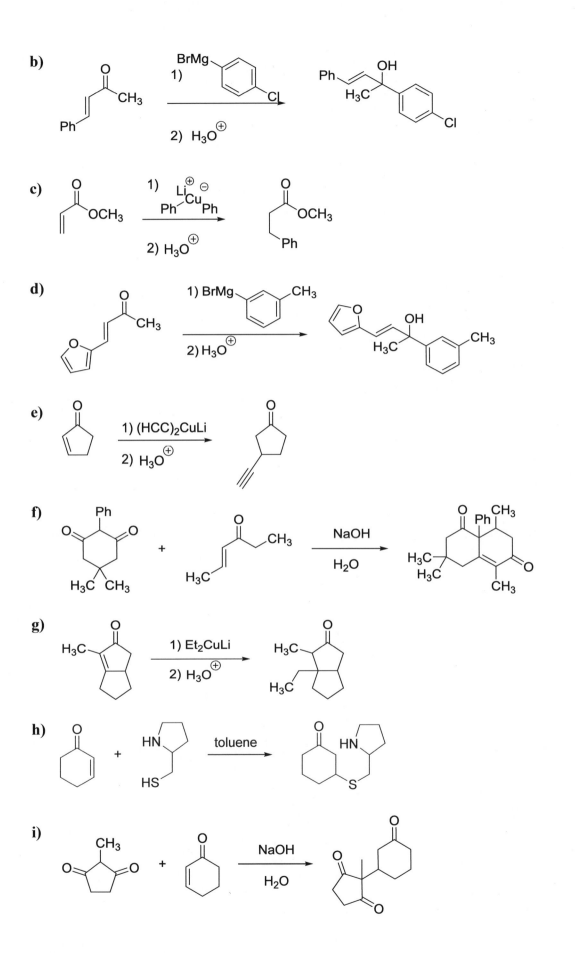

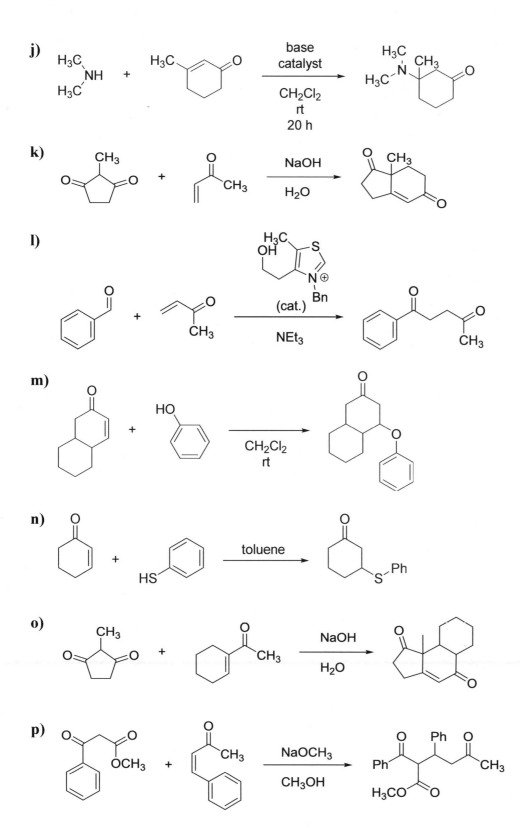

q)

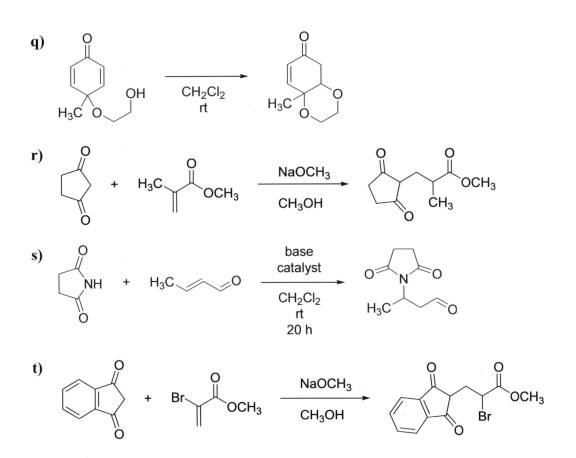

r)

s)

t)

18.25

Peracids are electrophilic and depend on reaction with a nucleophilic alkene. Because carbonyls are electron-withdrawing, unsaturated carbonyl compounds are poor nucleophiles. This reduces yield and allows for competing reactions. An alkene with an electron-withdrawing group is a good electrophile and can undergo epoxidation with nucleophilic reagents. Hydrogen peroxide can be deprotonated by hydroxide, making a nucleophilic oxygen with an OH leaving group that can be displaced by the resulting enolate.

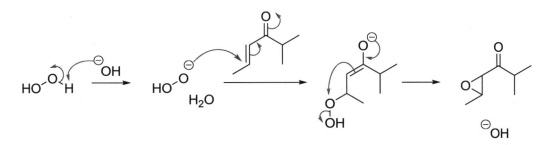

18.27

a) The excess base and inverse addition ensure that the kinetic enolate is formed and aldol addition occurs on the less substituted side.

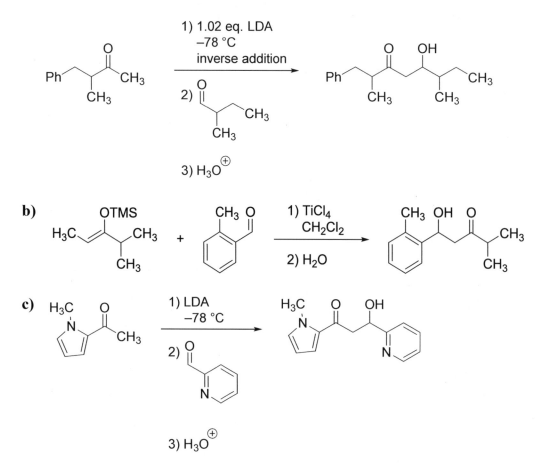

1) 1.02 eq. LDA
   −78 °C
   inverse addition

2) [aldehyde structure]

3) $H_3O^{\oplus}$

b)

OTMS structure + aldehyde

1) $TiCl_4$
   CH_2Cl_2

2) H_2O

c)

1) LDA
   −78 °C

2) [pyridine aldehyde]

3) $H_3O^{\oplus}$

d) The excess ketone compared to the base allows for equilibration and formation of the thermodynamic enolate. The aldol addition occurs on the more substituted side.

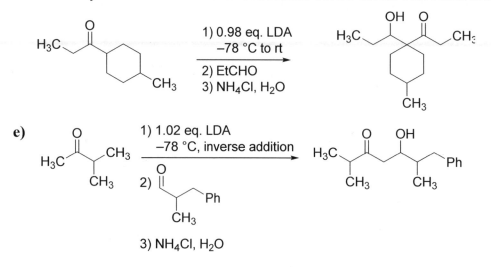

1) 0.98 eq. LDA
   −78 °C to rt

2) EtCHO

3) NH_4Cl, H_2O

e)

1) 1.02 eq. LDA
   −78 °C, inverse addition

2) [aldehyde structure] Ph, CH_3

3) NH_4Cl, H_2O

f)

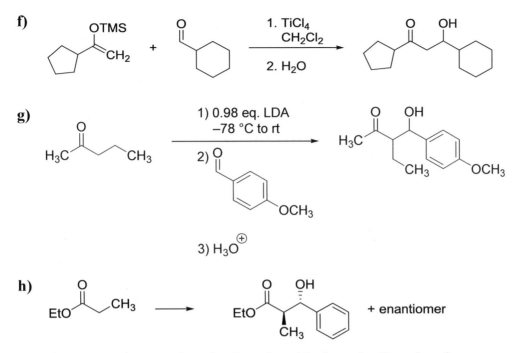

g)

h)

The *anti*-enolate requires the *E* enolate. To form the *E* enolate from an ester, the larger boron source and the smaller base are required. Removal of the boron and conversion of the alkoxide to an alcohol requires H_2O_2.

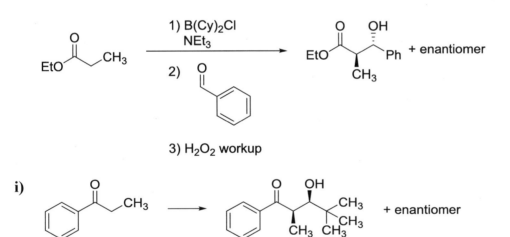

i)

The *syn*-aldol requires the *Z* enolate, which is formed from the small di-*n*-butyl boron and the larger EtN*i*-Pr$_2$ base. The added carbons come from the aldehyde.

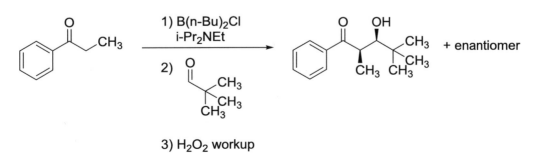

j)

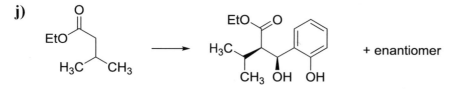

The product shown looks like a *syn*-enol; however, it is not in the proper orientation. It is actually an *anti*-aldol and requires the same conditions as the previous example. The added aldehyde must be the *p*-bromobenzaldehyde in order to add the bromophenyl.

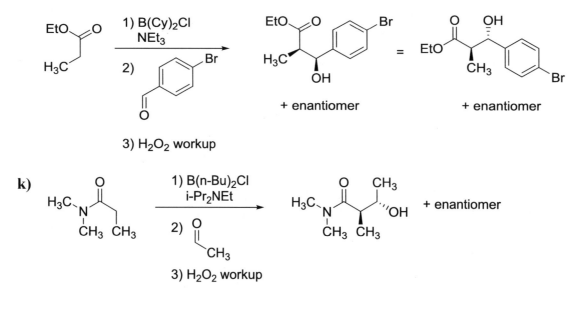

18.29

Forming the C–C bond involves the section shown in bold.

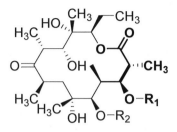

The indicated section, when reoriented to the standard conformation, is a *syn*-aldol.

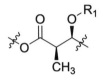

This requires the use of a *Z* enolate, which is formed from the smaller dialkyl boron with the larger base.

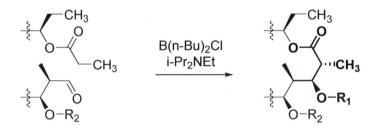

18.31

a)

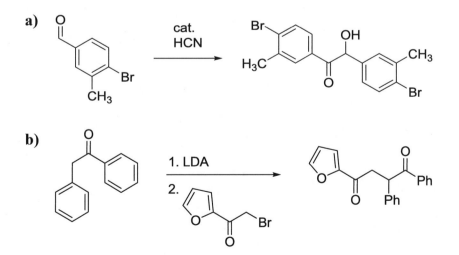

b)

c)

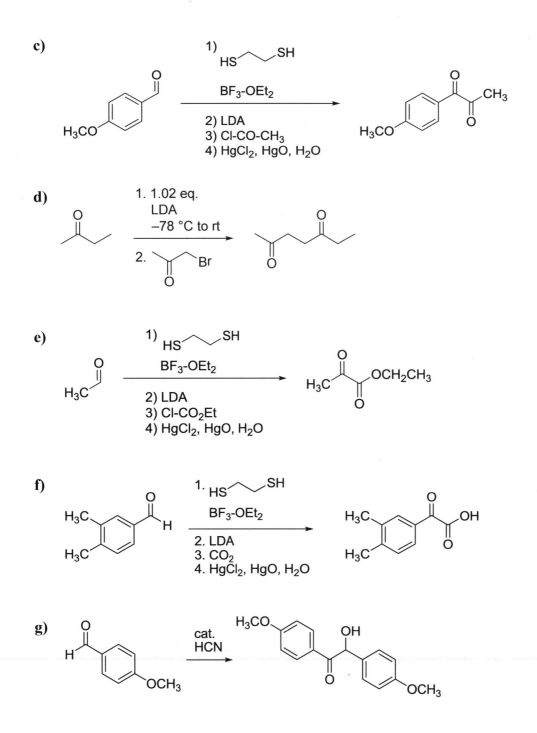

d)

e)

f)

g)

18.33

The dithiane hydrolysis follows the same pattern as the acetal hydrolysis mechanism, except that the sulfur atoms bond to mercury ions instead of hydrogen atoms.

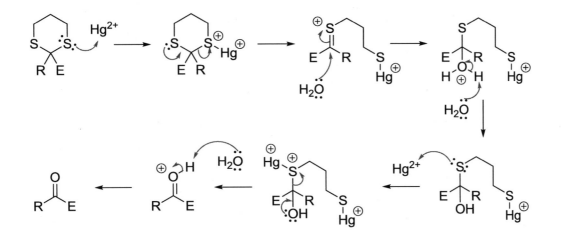

18.35

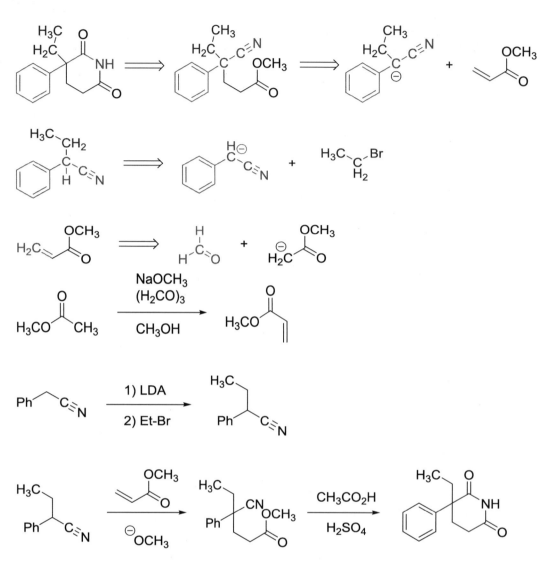

18.37

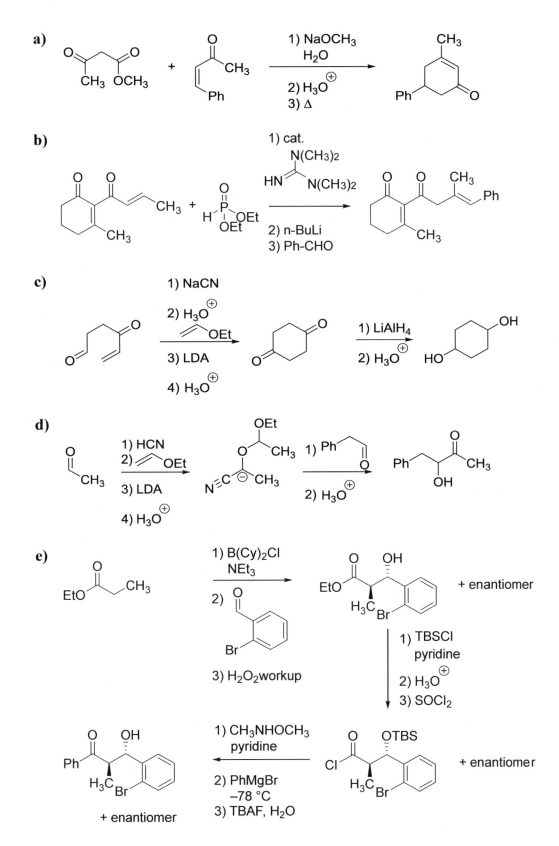

a)

b)

c)

d)

e)

18.39

Syntheses of compounds **A** and **B**:

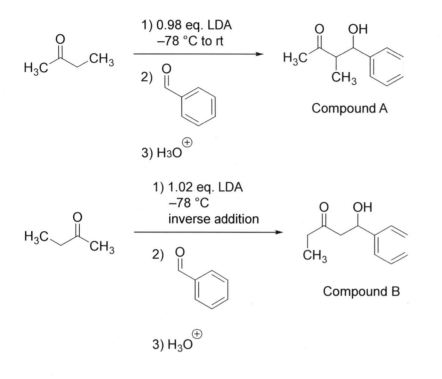

1) 0.98 eq. LDA
   −78 °C to rt

2) [benzaldehyde]

3) H₃O⁺

Compound A

1) 1.02 eq. LDA
   −78 °C
   inverse addition

2) [benzaldehyde]

3) H₃O⁺

Compound B

18.41

Answer: (d). Stabilized ylides are stabilized by an electron-withdrawing group. This eliminates (a) and (b) as possible answers. A standard Wittig reaction produces a *cis*-alkene; the addition of the electron-withdrawing group changes the mechanism to favour the *trans*-alkene, eliminating option (c).

18.43

Answer: (c). β-hydroxy ketones and 1,4-diketones have even-numbered dioxy relationships and are formed using umpolung reagents, eliminating (a) and (b) as possible answers. Cyclohexenones are formed from an intramolecular aldol condensation and are possible starting materials for a Michael reaction, eliminating option (d).

Challenge Problems

18.44

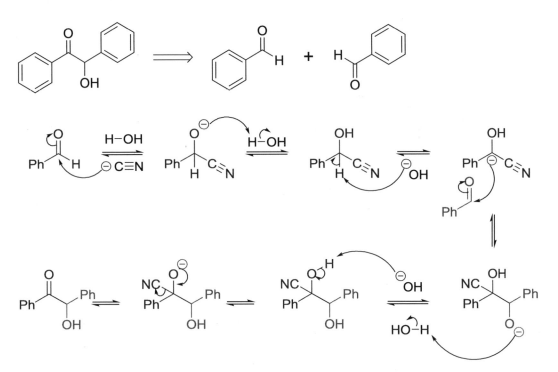

18.45

The section shown in bold is a 1,3-diol. The section shown in grey is a protected diol. Either could be formed from the reduction of a β-hydroxyketone. Depending on which hydroxyl is the result of reduction, the β-hydroxyketone could be either *syn* or *anti*, as shown below.

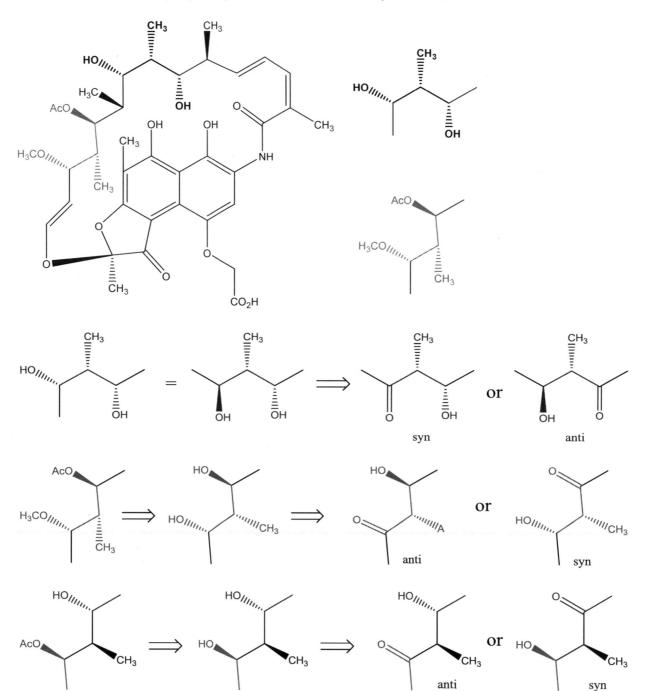

Chapter 19
Radicals:
Halogenation, Polymerization, and Reduction Reactions

PROBLEMS

19.5

a)

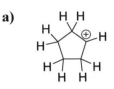

c)

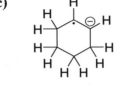

b)

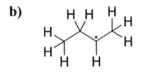

d)

19.7

a)

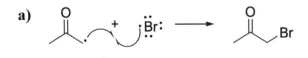

b)

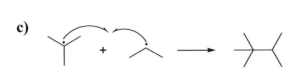

c)

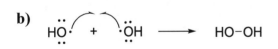

19.9

The polyunsaturated fatty acid can produce the most stable radical. Both of the double bonds can participate in resonance delocalization of the radical. The monounsaturated fatty acid would produce the next most stable radical (allylic) and the saturated fatty acid the least stable (2° carbon).

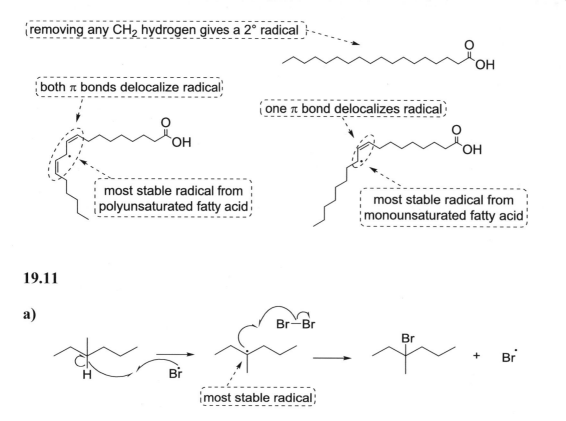

19.11

a)

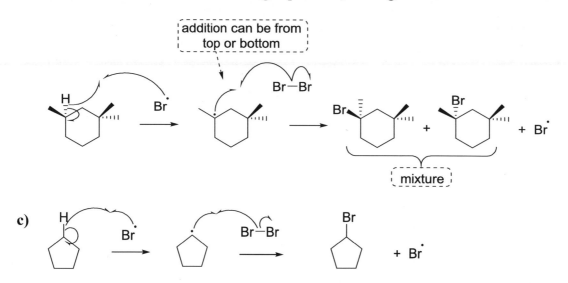

b) The most stable radical possible is tertiary. Due to the planar geometry of the radical, addition from both sides of the ring is possible, leading to a racemic mixture of enantiomers.

c)

d) The bridgehead hydrogen atoms are on chirality centres. The initial radical formation would remove one of them but leave the other. Addition of bromine can be from either side of the radical, which leads to a mixture of diastereomers.

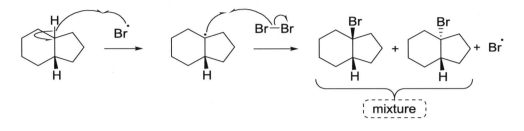

19.13

The benzylic position is the most reactive and its substitution leads to a racemic mixture of monobrominated product.

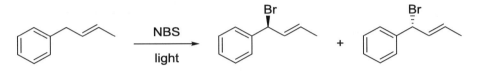

The benzylic radical formed is very stable due to resonance contributions from the double bond and the aromatic ring, and thus is the favoured pathway.

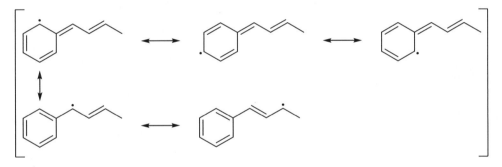

19.15

The 2-bromo product would be a Markovnikov addition to 1-hexene. Simple electrophilic HBr addition would give the desired product.

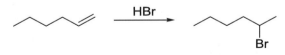

The 1-bromo product is an anti-Markovnikov product. Free radical hydrohalogenation is anti-Markovnikov and would give the required product.

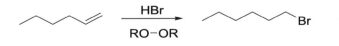

19.17

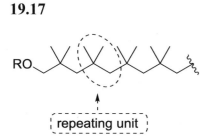

repeating unit

19.19

Initiation

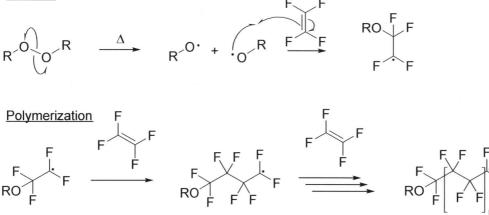

Polymerization

In order for branching to occur in the polytetrafluoroethylene (PTFE) polymerization reaction, a substituent on the main chain has to be abstracted by a radical. All of the substituents on the PTFE chain are very strongly bonded fluorine atoms and would be too difficult to remove in this fashion. So, branching is unlikely.

19.21

a)

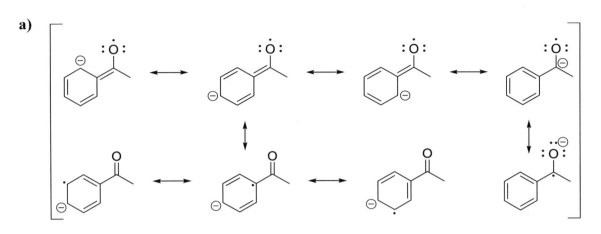

The most stable resonance form would have a fully aromatic ring and the negative charge located on the electronegative oxygen atom.

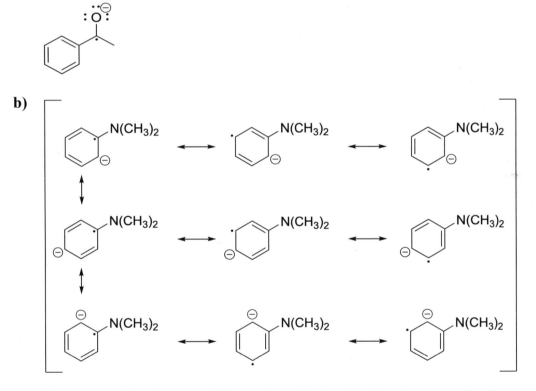

b)

The most stable form would have the radical and anion closest to the electronegative nitrogen.

19.23

The aromatic alcohol (also known as a *phenol*), (b), is most likely to donate a hydrogen since the radical formed can be stabilized through resonance.

19.25

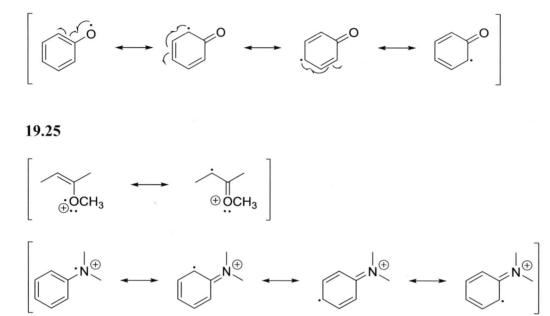

MCAT Style Problems

19.27

Answer: (d).

Challenge Problem

19.29

All of the mechanisms involve sequential transfer of electrons to the P450 enzyme and oxygen to the drug substrate. Note the increasing number of electrons on the iron centre represented by electron dots. This is a highly simplified version of the actual mechanism involved.

a) <u>Alkyl group of drug</u>

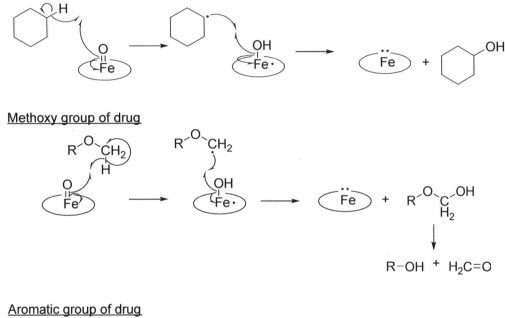

b) <u>Methoxy group of drug</u>

c) <u>Aromatic group of drug</u>

d) <u>Aromatic group of drug</u>

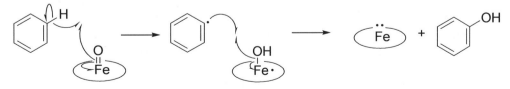

Chapter 20
Reactions Controlled by Orbital Interactions:
Ring Closures, Cycloadditions, and Rearrangements

PROBLEMS

20.21

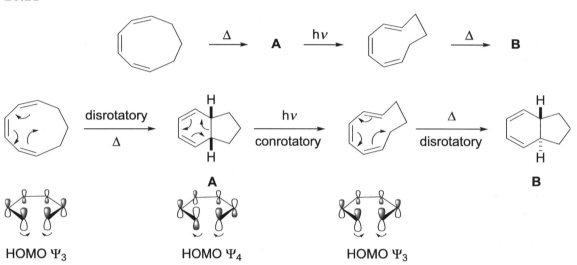

20.23

a) The bridgehead hydrogens are *syn*.

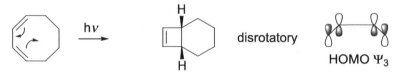

b) The hydrogens shown in the reactant are neither *anti* or *syn*.

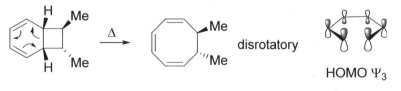

c) The hydrogens shown in the reactant are anti in the product.

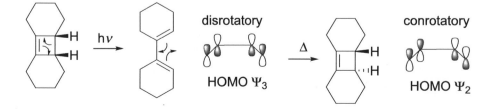

20.25

a)

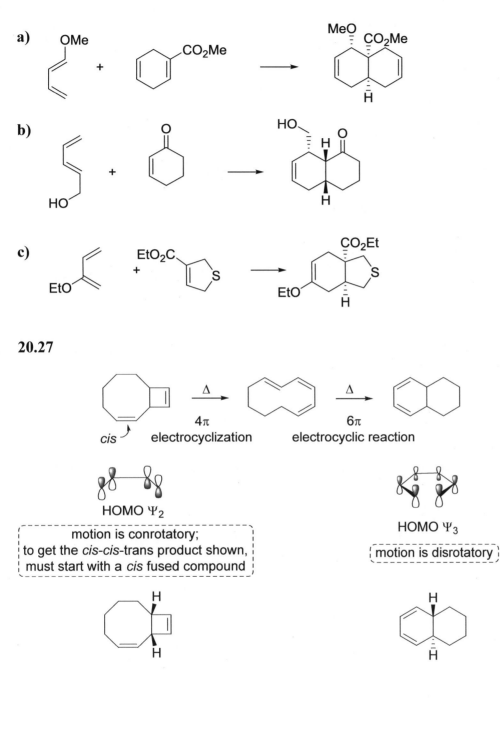

b)

c)

20.27

Δ
4π
electrocyclization

Δ
6π
electrocyclic reaction

cis

HOMO Ψ₂

motion is conrotatory;
to get the *cis-cis*-trans product shown,
must start with a *cis* fused compound

HOMO Ψ₃

motion is disrotatory

20.29

The product of ring closure has a large amount of ring string and so would be very high energy. The symmetry of the ring closure (conrotatory) would bring the two large alkyl substituents to the same side of the cyclobutene ring as well, causing more steric interactions.

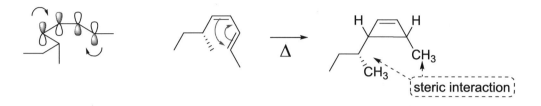

The [1,5] H migration does not have steric hindrance to contend with, so it is the preferred reaction mechanism.

20.31

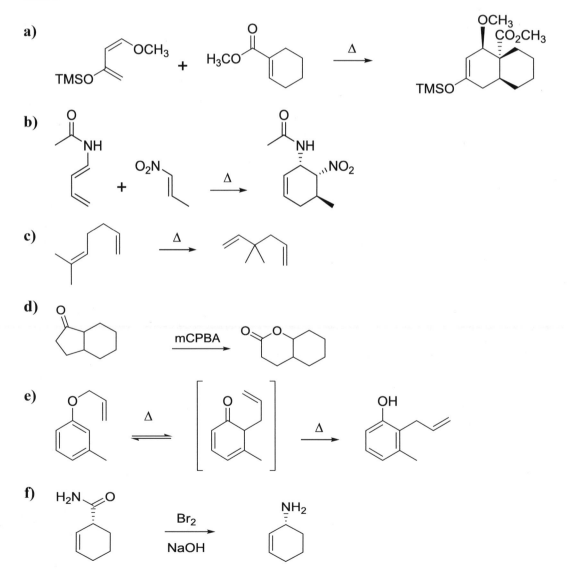

20.33

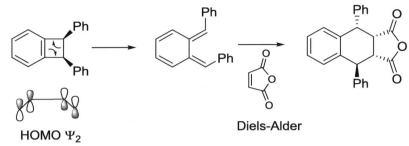

HOMO Ψ_2

motion is conrotatory

Diels-Alder

The conrotatory ring opening determines the diene geometry shown. The orientation of the phenyl groups in the diene means they will be *anti* in the Diels–Alder product. The dienophile addition is concerted, so the anhydride ring connections will have a *cis* geometry.

20.35

a)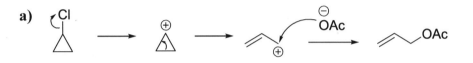

b) The ring opening would proceed through a three-membered ring carbocation, as in part (a). The HOMO for the product carbocation would be Ψ_1. In order for the p orbitals to be in phase in Ψ_1, the ring opening has to be disrotatory, as shown.

disrotatory

HOMO $\Psi 1$

The ring opening of the carbocation would give the following initial stereochemistry for the product carbocation.

disrotatory

20.37

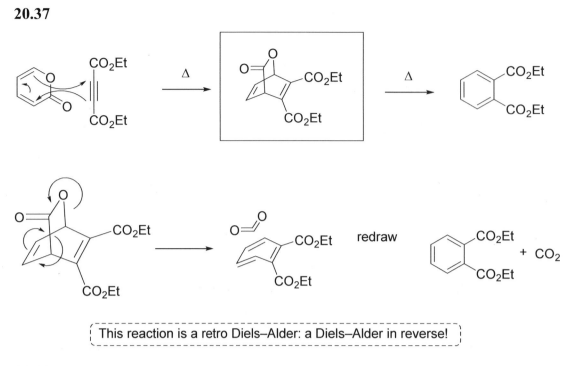

This reaction is a retro Diels–Alder: a Diels–Alder in reverse!

20.39

The first step can produce two regioisomers. Mechanisms for both possible sequences are shown below.

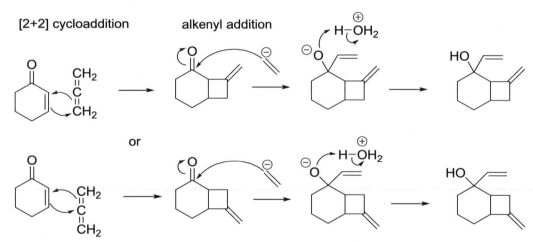

Only one of the final products has the double bonds in a geometry that can thermally rearrange. The [3,3] Cope rearrangement produces an enol. Tautomerization of the enol gives the final ketone product.

The final step is shown below.

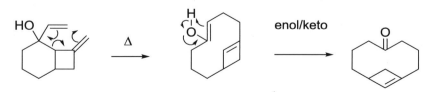

MCAT Style Problems

20.41

Answer: (c).

Challenge Problem

20.43

The proline can form an imine with the carbonyl carbon:

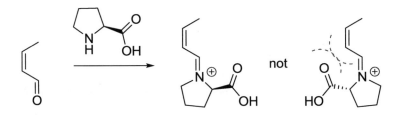

When the dienophile approaches from the *endo* direction, the carboxylic acid blocks approach from the top, only allowing approach from below the diene.

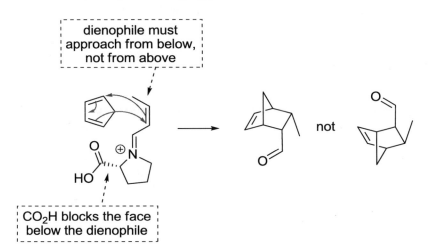